TRY THESE FOR MIND-OPENERS!

1. *There is three errers in this sentence.* Can you find them?

2. What is the largest sum of money in current United States coins (but no silver dollars, please) that a person can have in his pocket without being able to give someone change for a dollar, half-dollar, quarter, dime or nickel?

3. Plant ten trees in five rows of four trees each.

4. Most readers of this book are sexy. All readers of this book are superintelligent. Therefore:
   (a) Sexy readers of this book are also superintelligent.
   (b) Sex and superintelligence don't mix well.
   (c) All superintelligent readers of this book are sexy.
   (d) Most readers of this book are superintelligent about sex.

Also by James F. Fixx and
available in Popular Library editions:

GAMES FOR THE SUPERINTELLIGENT

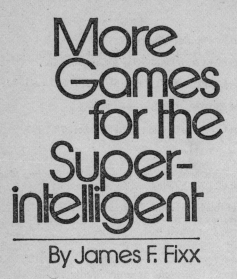

More Games for the Super-intelligent

By James F. Fixx

POPULAR LIBRARY • NEW YORK

Published by Popular Library, CBS Publications,
CBS Consumer Publishing, a Division of CBS Inc.,
by arrangement with Doubleday & Company, Inc.

November, 1977

Library of Congress Catalog Card Number: 76-7695

ISBN: 0-445-04114-5

Portions of this book originally appeared in *Playboy Magazine,*
Copyright © 1972 by Playboy Enterprises, Inc.

Portions of this book originally appeared in
Games for the Superintelligent

For Alice,
who is superintelligent
in the only way that really counts

PRINTED IN THE UNITED STATES OF AMERICA

A word of welcome—
and of warning

There are, I have discovered, two kinds of people in the world: those who love puzzles and those who can't stand them.* This would hardly be worth bringing up if it were not for the fact that the two camps are so distinct, and indeed even hostile, as to present more than ordinary dangers for the unwary. Puzzles lovers, despite the convolutions and complexities of their minds, tend in one respect to be quite simple people. We naïvely assume that because *we* like puzzles, and because puzzles seem to us so self-evidently pleasurable, surely everybody must like them. In fact, however, everybody does no such thing. On the contrary, many people, upon being shown a puzzle, even one of unquestionable excellence, will turn upon it— and upon us—with such scorn that we are

* There are also, of course, two *other* kinds of people in the world: those who believe there are two kinds of people in the world and those who do not. That, however, is an entirely different subject.

likely to think long and hard before proffering another one. I myself have seen the eyes of more than one friend glaze over with boredom when confronted with my enthusiasm for puzzles. I even know of a marriage whose untimely dissolution was at least partly attributable to one of the partners' overfondness for mental recreations, and another in which one member, finally grown impatient at her spouse's insistence that she share his intellectual romps, was driven to declare, "If you ever show me another one of those puzzles I swear I'm going to move as far away from you as I can. Maybe to Pago Pago." (He did and she did, though not to Pago Pago. The anecdote seems to me, however, to lose little of its force because of that minor imperfection.)

Such misadventures are clearly indicative of strong feelings—ones we toy with at our peril. Be forewarned, therefore: the mere fact that you are reading this book by no means grants you license to urge its contents on those who are not similarly committed. The only safe procedure is to acknowledge the fact that in your liking for puzzles you are different from other people. Revel privately, if you want to, in that difference, but do not—under any circumstances—undertake even the gentlest of proselytizing. That way lies nothing but disaster. Remember: you are an intellectual at play, not a missionary.

The sort of hostility I am speaking of is

nothing new. As long ago as the tenth century, an Arab traveler named Ibn Fadlan, visiting the Volga Bulgars, reported: "When they observe a man who excels through quickwittedness and knowledge, they ... seize him, put a rope around his neck and hang him on a tree where he is left until he rots away." Lest anyone wonder why the Bulgars recoiled so strongly from any display of excessive intelligence, Zeki Validi Togan, an authority on Ibn Fadlan, explains: "There is nothing mysterious about the cruel treatment meted out by the Bulgars to people who were overly clever. It was based on the simple, sober reasoning of the average citizens who wanted only to lead what they considered to be a normal life, and to avoid any risk or adventure in which the 'genius' might lead them."

As the intelligentsia of Ibn Fadlan's time learned to their distress, the temptation to share one's enthusiasms is always great— sometimes too great. When a thing gives us as much pleasure as puzzles and other mental diversions can, it is only natural that we should want to spread the word. Resist that temptation. I speak from experience. Some time ago, on a beach near Sarasota, Florida, I was using a conch shell to sketch a puzzle in the sand for a friend. It was a complicated puzzle, and I had covered considerable wind-swept acreage with diagrams, charts, and computations when I paused to look up—just in time to see my friend pile the last of his beach gear into his car and drive off.

That sort of thing has an ugly way of sticking in your mind. What lesson, if any, can we draw from it? Well, for one thing it suggests, I think, that we must choose our puzzle companions with care. We must not assume, until we have seen irrefutable evidence of it, the presence of an enthusiasm that may not exist at all. Rather, those of us who share an interest in puzzles should stick quietly together, welcoming outsiders whenever they chance to turn up, but never taking it for granted that they will. (They usually won't.) I have discovered, just as you no doubt have, that fooling around with puzzles is an essentially solitary pastime. In the predecessor to this book, *Games for the Superintelligent*, I briefly mentioned the solitariness of the puzzler's lot and was instantly awash in correspondents grateful at having found some kindred spirits at last. The loneliness of the puzzler is, it seems, an inseparable part of his condition.

This view was convincingly buttressed just as I was getting ready to write these words. In a letter from Oak Park, Illinois, a reader wrote as follows:

I greatly enjoyed your book. Although I never have considered myself a genius, your discussion of the problems encountered by very bright people had a familiar ring. I tried every problem in your book and solved a large number of them. This was a great boost to my spirit. I have never been much of a conversationalist, nor a mixer. Frankly, most people bore me after a short time, and I had always wondered why this was and what was wrong with me and why I was different. I will be forever grateful to you for helping me find some answers to my questions.

Not everyone, of course, is going to find answers to his fundamental puzzlements about life in a book like this one. What most people *will* find is something quite different, though in its way it is also valuable: a kind of puzzle not readily available elsewhere. The title of this volume is, needless to say, something of a jape, intended (1) to flatter the reader and (2) to suggest that he will in turn be flattering anyone for whom he buys it as a gift. Yet, that ugly little secret having been confessed, there remains one sense in which the title is quite accurate: these are a peculiar sort of puzzle. They all have a proven appeal for extremely bright people, either the members of Mensa, the high-I.Q. society whose puzzles inspired *Games for the Superintelligent,* or else the young professional men and women who subscribe to the four magazines for which I have edited a monthly puzzle column for some three years now.* The puzzles are all, furthermore, rigorously logical and, except for those in Chapter VI, free from trickery and attempts to mislead. They are, furthermore, essentially simple, requiring no advanced mathematics and no knowledge of esoteric logical principles. Finally, they all have a clean, spare elegance: they are not rock but plainsong.

If your tastes are at all like mine, you'll enjoy these puzzles. Most puzzle books, even those intended for more or less intelligent readers, are woefully unappealing. The other day, while doing a bit of rearranging in my library, I found myself trying to gather all my puzzle books together in one place. They made a considerable pile, but not, I am sorry to say, a very interesting one. Most of the books seemed to have been put together by worshipers of mere doggedness, the sort of people who find it fun to hunt for hidden words in bleak and meaningless prairies of jumbled letters. The words can be found, of course, but to what purpose? When you are through, all you have proved is that you can keep your mind on a dull subject for a long time.

But *de gustibus,* etc. If people enjoy that

* *Juris Doctor* (for lawyers), *MBA* (business executives), *Medical Dimensions* (doctors), and *New Engineer* (engineers of all types). Together they reach several hundred thousand readers, most of them, to judge by the mail I receive, both enthusiastic about puzzles and impressively knowledgeable about them.

sort of thing, let us rejoice on their behalf. Pleasure, any pleasure, is all too rare in this world. Yet we need not seek to share that particular pleasure. I have, on the contrary, taken pains to avoid that kind of puzzle, on the grounds that an intricate and precise logical excursion, however brief, is more rewarding than a whole afternoon spent slogging purposelessly through some protracted problem fit only for drones. I make no apology for taking this severe and limited view of things. There are plenty of books for the drones and far too few for you and me.

A word about how this volume is arranged. It seems to me that, since human intelligence is our subject, we ought first to try to reach some agreement on exactly what it is. Accordingly, the first chapter takes us into that fascinating and perennially controversial mine field. There follow several sizable clumps of puzzles of various types—mathematical, verbal, logical, and so forth—all of them arranged to give the reader's mind a varied and vigorous regimen of calisthenics. Since some readers, by the time they are this far into things, may well be wondering why they are having trouble with certain puzzles and not with others, they will next find a chapter dealing with the techniques of puzzle solving; it gives, among other things, a good many examples of the ways extremely bright people attack a puzzle and how their minds differ from those of the less nimble-witted among us. Finally, in Chapter IX, you will find an intelligence test that will give an indication of your fitness for membership in perhaps the most exclusive intellectual club the world has ever known: Mensa. To join, you don't need wealth, looks, or even good manners. All you need is an I.Q. in the top 2 per cent of the population. If you measure up, you may find the organization just the thing for learning what your mind is made of. If, either because of heredity or inclination, the verbal hurly-burly of Mensa isn't your kind of competition, do at least stay for the preliminary rounds in Chapters I to VIII. You could, in spite of yourself, discover that what you had always thought was just gray matter is really something considerably more colorful.

JAMES F. FIXX

Riverside, Connecticut
January 1976

Contents

I

What, exactly, is intelligence?

Even though you and I have a fairly clear idea of what we mean when we use the word "intelligence," there has never been much scholarly agreement on just what intelligence really is. Sir Francis Galton, a pioneer investigator of the human brain and the author of *Hereditary Genius: An Enquiry into its Laws and Consequences* (1869), thought of intelligence as being made up of three separate qualities—"intellect," "zeal," and "power of work." C. E. Spearman, the inventor of factor analysis and author of *The Abilities of Man* (1927), considered intelligence to be something—he called it simply *g*—accounting for the fact that a person who does well at one thing is also likely to do well at other things. L. L. Thurstone, the author of *The Nature of Intelligence* (1924), believed intelligence to be composed of precisely seven capacities, verbal ability, verbal fluency, numerical ability, spatial ability, perceptual ability, inductive reasoning, and memory. On the other hand,

J. P. Guilford, a psychologist who has had considerable influence during the past quarter century, purported to find in intelligence no fewer than 120 abilities, which he cross-classified into (a) the types of information each customarily handles, (b) the process by which it handles it, and (c) the nature of what emerges. Other researchers, a bit less ambitiously, have tried to get off to a solid start by offering workable definitions of intelligence, but with equally disparate results. It has, for example, been called "the ability to carry on abstract thinking" by L. M. Terman, "the capacity to acquire capacity" by Herbert Woodrow, and "innate general cognitive ability" by C. L. Burt. Spearman called it "the ability to educe relations and correlates," and James McKeen Cattell tried to clarify matters by distinguishing between "fluid" and "crystallized" intelligence.

Intelligence is unquestionably a curiously elusive human capacity. Any one of us can easily recognize intelligence when we encounter it, and can unhesitatingly judge, furthermore, whether it is in deficient supply or is present in abundance. Yet those who have devoted their lives to its study cannot tell us whether it is one thing of 120 separate things and cannot, for that matter, even agree on a definition. It is, however, too easy, as well as distinctly misleading, to make a joke of what is a serious, fundamentally valid, and certainly arduous enterprise. Coming to grips with intelligence is no easy task. The chief problem is that it is not directly observable. We cannot place calipers on it to measure it, nor can an anatomist evaluate it at an autopsy. It is detectable, if it is detectable at all, only in the results it produces. The Encyclopedia Britannica calls it a "hypothetical construct" and points out that even I.Q., which many imagine to be a quite unambiguous assessment of a person's intelligence, is nothing more than a "representation" of intelligence. A representation, it goes without saying, may be quite unlike the real thing.

Part of the difficulty arises from the fact that intelligence—and its more awesome partner, genius—got off to a bad start, or at any rate a late one. Although the early Babylonian writers and the Greek philosophers discussed the intellect, the mind, and related questions, the present-day concept of intelligence was unknown until the early years of the twentieth century. The word "genius," in the sense in which we most commonly use it today, did not even appear in Samuel Johnson's exhaustive dictionary of 1755. (The 1971 OED, which does of course include it, defines it as "native intellectual power of an exalted type, such as is attributed to those who are esteemed greatest in any department of art, speculation, or practice; instinctive and extraordinary capacity for imaginative creation, original thought, invention, or discovery," and goes on to observe

17

that it is "often contrasted with *talent*.") Intelligence, it seems, was a subject that simply did not arise until the twentieth century's analytical spirit finally called it into being.

When that happened, it was only natural that researchers should be as interested in measuring its dimensions as in describing how it works. Our age, after all, is one in which it is seen as a proper function of scholarship not just to explain Shakespeare but, using computers, to dissect him syllable by syllable—and there are no doubt some who, if a choice had to be made, would argue that the latter should take precedence. So the Intelligence Quotient—that number that haunts our lives from kindergarten to crypt—was born. In concept anyway, the I.Q. seems quite straightforward. To start with, one assumes that intelligence is distributed along a Gaussian curve, with perhaps slightly more people at the low-I.Q. end to account for brain damage (which diminishes I.Q. but does not, so far as we know, ever raise it). If we let 100 represent average intelligence, then 50 per cent of the world's population is seen to have I.Q.s between 90 and 110, 68 per cent between 85 and 115, 14 per cent between 116 and 130, and 2 per cent above 130. If, then, we devise reliable I.Q. tests, each of us can readily be placed in his proper place on the bellshaped curve and can enjoy the benefits—or endure the consequences—appro-

18

priate to that station. It all seems to make a good deal of sense.

Unfortunately, the first I.Q. test had scarcely been devised (by the French psychologist Alfred Binet, in 1905) than a backlash began to set in. By midcentury it was at full strength. In 1958 David Wechsler, chief psychologist at Bellevue Psychiatric Hospital, was writing (in *The Measurement and Appraisal of Adult Intelligence*), "In recent years the I.Q. has lost caste. There has been a growing tendency among clinical psychologists to pay only scant attention to the I.Q. as such." More recently, I.Q. tests have come in for heavy criticism on political grounds. In his recent book *The Science and Politics of I.Q.*, Leon J. Kamin defines the issue succinctly: "The I.Q. test in America, and the way in which we think about it, has been fostered by men committed to a particular social view. That view includes the belief that those on the bottom are genetically inferior victims of their own immutable defects. The consequence has been that the I.Q. test has served as an instrument of oppression against the poor—dressed in the trappings of science, rather than politics. The message of science is heard respectfully, particulary when the tidings it carries are soothing to the public conscience." Far from being, as one American psychologist has called it, "psychology's most telling accomplishment," the I.Q. test is, in this view, wickedly fraudulent.

One need not be a psychologist to discern another way in which I.Q. tests can be misleading. Most people, especially laymen, customarily refer to a person's I.Q. as if it were always a valid indication of ability. But a moment's reflection will reveal that it is no such thing. We all know people of unquestioned brilliance who can hardly cross the street without endangering their lives (it is for good reason that the absentminded professor is a persistent folk figure) and other people who, although commanding a vast body of information and uncommon mental agility, are scarcely able to earn a living. There is, in short, not necessarily much of a correlation between I.Q. and ability. The most sophisticated psychologists are, of course, well aware of this and put little emphasis on I.Q. in the absence of other information about a person. Writes Wechsler: "Individuals having the same I.Q.'s may differ considerably in their actual or potential capacity for intelligent behavior." He leaves no doubt about exactly what he means: "Every reader will be able to recall persons of high intellectual ability in some particular field whom they would unhesitatingly characterize as below average in general intelligence."

If, then, the experts are not agreed on just what intelligence is, and if, furthermore, the dowsing rod that is supposed to find it doesn't work after all, can we even presume to discuss it? Can it be of any possible interest to us? Can we make any use of the concept, fuzzy as it plainly is? The answer to all three questions is: Of course we can. Psychologists may tie themselves into knots trying to define intelligence, and they may worry about what precisely belongs in the recipe, whether a single ingredient or 120 of them, but as a practical matter you and I know we have no such difficulty. We freely discuss intelligence with each other, knowing at least in a general way what we are talking about. (If our talk lacks scientific precision, that is only because we ordinarily have no need for such precision. I do not need to know the words *Cyanocitta cristata* in order to tell you there is a blue jay in my bird feeder.) Furthermore, we have little difficulty in agreeing on what constitutes intelligence and what does not. We are amazed, perhaps, by the story of Jacques Inaudi, whom Binet studied at length in 1892 and 1893 because in fifteen minutes the young man could do mathematical calculations that would have taken a first-rate mathematician fifteen days. But we never mistake such isolated abilites for the sort of broad intelligence possessed by Leonardo da Vinci or Newton or, in our own time, Einstein.

We can agree, too, on at least one other thing: intelligence is well worth having. Intelligence has, to be sure, landed more than a few of its possessors in deep trouble. One thinks, for example, of the student who on a physics examination was asked to describe a method for determining the height of a building by using a barometer. Finding the expected answer obvious and uninteresting, he outraged the educational authorities by giving two alternate methods: (1) drop the barometer off the building's roof and time the interval until it smashes on the ground; (2) find the owner of the building and say to him, "If you tell me how tall your building is, I will give you a good barometer."* One thinks, too, of the seventeenth-century Dominican friar Giordano Bruno, who was offered one opportunity after another to renounce the heresies of Copernicanism and thereby save his life. Ultimately Bruno, unwilling to violate what his vast, inquiring intellect told him must be true, was burned at the stake by the Inquisition.

For the most part, however, such painful exceptions notwithstanding, intelligence is beyond question something to be prized. Studies show that those who are gifted as children earn above-average incomes as adults, enjoy better mental and physical health, and do better both in school and at work. Not long ago a Stanford University professor, Dr. Pauline S. Sears, reported on the results of a continuing study of 430 women who, as teen-agers

* Eddie Epstein of New York City proposes a third method: find the owner of the building and say to him, "If you don't tell me how tall your building is, I'll break this barometer over your head."

in California in the 1920s, were in the top 1 per cent of the population in intelligence. (The study, regarded as a classic, was begun in 1921–22 by Stanford psychologist L. M. Terman.) Dr. Sears found that 67 per cent of them had earned bachelors' degrees (8 per cent is typical for their age group) and that they had, by their own testimony, lived more satisfying lives than would have been the case had they been less intellectually gifted. "It may well be," she wrote in a report on the study, "that the coping mechanisms which enable gifted women to adapt flexibly to a variety of conditions . . . are related to the intelligence they bring to their life situations."

One need not, however, take so pragmatic a view of intelligence in order to find it worth while. In his lively and wideranging study, *Anti-Intellectualism in American Life*, Richard Hofstadter refers to the capacity for intellectual "playfulness": "The intellectual relishes the play of the mind for its own sake and finds in it one of the major values in life. What one thinks of here is the element of sheer delight in intellectual activity. Seen in this guise, intellect may be taken as the healthy animal spirits of the mind, which come into exercise when the surplus of mental energies is released from the tasks required for utility and mere survival. . . . Veblen spoke often of the intellectual faculty as 'idle curiosity'—but this is a misnomer in so far as the curiosity of the playful mind is inordinately restless and active. This very restlessness and activity gives a distinctive cast to its view of truth and its discontent with dogmas." Intelligence, it is plain, finds abundant justification not in (to use Hofstadter's archly playful word) "mere" usefulness but in pure frolicsomeness and *joie de vivre*.

We thus find ourselves in the curious position of children who, seeing a person eat an unknown food, want some for themselves and start screaming for it: we may not know what intelligence is but we want more of it— for ourselves, certainly, but especially for our offspring. But how much more can we have? Is it possible to enhance or increase what we have been given? It is easy to agree with Leonardo's observation: "Iron rusts from disuse, stagnant water loses its purity and in cold weather becomes frozen; even so does inaction sap the vigors of the mind." But is the corollary equally true? Can exercise, perhaps certain mental disciplines, stimulate the vigors of the mind?

Many people would say yes. "There is a technique, a knack, for thinking...," Charles P. Curtis, Jr., and Ferris Greenslet wrote in their charming anthology *The Practical Cogitator*. "You are not wholly at the mercy of your thoughts.... They are a machine you can learn to operate." Similarly, Win Wenger, in his recent book *How to Increase Your Intelligence*, has little doubt that we can improve our I.Q.s. Noting that intelligence is the result of heredity (80 per cent or so) and environment (the remaining 20 per cent or so), and that these seem to be more or less rigidly fixed at an early age, Wenger is nonetheless certain we can do something about our intelligence: "There is a misconception that we are born with a certain intelligence and are trapped forever in the narrow range that is determined to be our 'I.Q.' The truth of the matter is that unless we are taught to use our brains, unless we fully understand how our brains work and their relationship to intelligence, we may never even approach truly intelligent functioning. Within all of us is the potential for genius."*

This seems to me rather doubtful. Geniuses, by definition, are so extraordinary that it takes very little acquaintance with even a single genius to realize that most of us are light-years from their mental estate. I once had the opportunity of working closely with a person who was unquestionably a genius. He had a nimble, inventive, and above all tireless mind, and one of my strongest memories is of watching our little staff, myself included, crumble into collapsed quiescence as the night wore on, while he remained as fresh as he had been when he

* Wenger's is a heady and uplifting doctrine. But not every reader, I suspect, will be inclined to follow every aspect of the intellectual regimen he prescribes—particularly when it comes to such I.Q.-raising techniques as hanging upside down with your eyes closed (to improve circulation in the brain and build up its "balancing centers") and brachiation, or swinging from one overhead handhold to another like an ape (to "turn on" the cortex).

showed up for work that morning. "He seems," a staff member remarked after one particularly long night, "to have some secret source of energy that no one else has learned how to draw on." As a chronic and lifelong eight-hour sleeper, I cannot imagine anything (even brachiation) that could possibly boost me to the kind of sleepless genius my colleague enjoyed.

On the other hand, there seems little doubt that one can improve the functioning of the brain at least to some extent. In my own case, I have been studying puzzles and I.Q. tests for so long that even the toughest and trickiest of them are likely to be more or less familiar to me. By one definition, then (I.Q. is what an I.Q. test tests), my I.Q. has indeed improved. I grant you that the improvement is largely spurious—being able to solve a tricky puzzle does not, after all, equip a person to live more rationally—but in this one respect my brain is a more efficient instrument. That sort of improvement is within the reach of anyone who wants to take the trouble.

Whether it is worth taking the trouble for is the question. Many experts would argue that it is not. David Wechsler summarily disposes of such ambitions by his reference to *artificially* raising the I.Q. test *score* (the emphasis is his), clearly implying a distinction between actual I.Q. and one's I.Q. score. To raise the score without affecting the I.Q. is much like congratulating yourself on having grown taller merely because you've bought yourself a pair of elevator shoes.

Other mental techniques, however, confer more solid benefits. The German physicist Helmholtz, whose researches ranged widely over the whole landscape of science, once told how important new thoughts came to him. He described three steps. The first he called Preparation, in which he investigated the problem "in all directions." The second was Incubation, in which he did no conscious thinking about the problem. The third he called Illumination; it was then that "happy ideas come unexpectedly without effort, like an inspiration." Helmholtz went on to remark, "So far as I am concerned, they have never come to me when my mind was fatigued, or when I was at my working table." Ideas came most easily to him, he said, during a walk in the woods on a sunny day. Arthur Koestler described much the same process in *The Act of Creation*; its general outlines will be familiar to anyone who, working with his brain, must rely not just on doggedness but on an occasional flicker of inspiration.

Graham Wallas, an English economist who was much concerned with the role of the subconscious, thought the process Helmholtz describes could be consciously controlled. "Men have known for thousands of years," he wrote, "that conscious effort and its resulting habits can be used to improve the thought-processes of young persons, and have formulated for that purpose an elaborate art of education. The 'educated' man can in consequence, 'put his mind on to a chosen subject, and 'turn his mind off' in a way which is impossible to an uneducated man." Wallas suggested that the problem-solving process can be made more efficient by starting to work on several problems in succession, then laying them aside, rather then trying to solve a problem at one sitting.* The important thing is that there be a period of freedom from the demands of the problem at hand, a time of leisure and even of idleness. How much may Darwin's lifelong poor health, and his consequent need for frequent rest, have contributed to his achievements?

Although the need for occasional leisured stretches is well known to creative people, it is a constant source of perplexity, and at

* Wallas offers two enlightening illustrations, one showing what the Helmholtz technique can accomplish, the other showing what happens when it is ignored: "A well-known academic psychologist . . . , who was also a preacher, told me that he found by experience that his Sunday sermon was much better if he posed the problem on Monday, than if he did so later in the week, although he might give the same number of hours of conscious work to it in each case. It seems to be a tradition among practicing barristers to put off any consideration of each brief to the latest possible moment before they have to deal with it, and to forget the whole matter as rapidly as possible after dealing with it. This fact may help to explain a certain want of depth which has often been noticed in the typical lawyer-statesman, and which may be due to his conscious thought not being sufficiently extended and enriched by subconscious thought."

times impatience, to those who must pay their salaries. I once worked for a publishing company whose president—a businessman at heart, rather than a man of letters—had collected a whole filing drawer full of techniques for prodding indolent writers and editors into giving him a fair day's work. Over the years he had clipped them out of *Advertising Age*, management magazines, and the plethora of newsletters he subscribed to, and he felt that his way with "the creatives," as he called them, was largely attributable to the techniques he had derived from these sources. He had, for one thing, read somewhere that creatives like money as much as anyone else, and he had hopes of someday devising a financial incentive plan for them, much like the commission or bonus arrangement used with salesmen. Once, in an effort to stir a sluggish artist into action, he worked out a custom-tailored plan of Talmudic complexity. When the artist, unmoved, went on as usual, the president confided to me, "Creatives aren't like other people."

He was, of course, right. While writers, editors, painters, composers, and other thinkers may indeed like money as much as anyone else, they are not appreciably moved or motivated by it because in the nature of things they cannot be. When I am seated at my typewriter and the words refuse to come—when, let us say, I am tired or preoccupied or out of sorts—I would welcome a raise in

29

pay but it would almost certainly not improve my work. What does sometimes improve my work is resort to the Helmholtz principle. If I lay the difficulty aside for a time, when I return to it I will in all likelihood find myself able to tackle it with surprising ease. Although this principle is widely applicable, it is one that not many people ever discover—an unfortunate lapse, since using it is precisely equivalent to increasing your intelligence.

The enhancement of intelligence is not, however, without its difficulties and even dangers. This is nowhere truer than in the United States. From the very beginning, the egalitarian idea upon which the nation was founded tended to inhibit any manifestation of extraordinary intelligence. If every man was just as good as every other man, so ran the unexpressed argument, every man was also just as ordinary. With the growing sentiment for universal suffrage in the nineteenth century, the common man began to assume a particularly exalted position. "If reason is a universal faculty," wrote George Bancroft, a nineteenth-century historian who was much involved in the politics of his time, "the universal decision is the nearest criterion of truth. The common mind winnows opinions; it is the sieve which separates error from certainty." Important as this idea unquestionably was in the development of democracy, it did little to enhance the life of the mind. "Anti-intellectualism," observes one historian, "is founded in the democratic institutions and the egalitarian sentiments of this country."

This strain in American life, though persistent, is not, however, quite as anti-intellectual as its critics sometimes pretend. If it were, we might have less to worry about than we actually do. Anti-intellectualism, after all, implies a certain intellectual stance, however wrongheaded. What we find in the United States is something more insidious than anti-intellectualism: a persistent lack of interest in things intellectual. Hofstadter puts it well: "The public is not simply divided into intellectual and anti-intellectual factions. The greater part of the public, and a great part even of the intelligent and alert public, is simply non-intellectual." In his classic study *The Organization Man* (1956), William H. Whyte, Jr., suggests how this attitude manifests itself in business. He cites, as one example, a well-known chemical company's recruiting film. At one point, as three scientists are shown in a laboratory, a narrator comments: "No geniuses here—just a bunch of average Americans working together."

In such a climate, it is scarcely surprising that intelligent people often feel that they receive less recognition than is their due. Not long ago I had a chance to speak with a group of extremely bright adults in New York City. All had I.Q.s of about 150; all worked for large companies; and all spoke feelingly

31

of the necessity for disguising from their superiors the true scope of their mental abilities. "I've found that it's safer," a bearded technician in his thirties said, "not to make waves. Unless you've got a very bright boss, which I don't, you'll just make him feel insecure. I used to try to point out better ways of doing things, but I found that it usually works out better if I keep my ideas to myself." Others in the group echoed his lament.

Our educational system does little to help. In general, it does not do much to raise bright people to their potential nor does it significantly help people of average intelligence understand and appreciate those who are more intelligent than themselves. Though much lip service is given to the importance of educating gifted young people, things have not really changed much in the decade and a half since Jerome S. Bruner, the noted Harvard education professor, wrote that "the top quarter of public school students, from which we must draw intellectual leadership in the next generation, is perhaps the most neglected by our school. . . ."

The problem is as much a matter of attitude as of practice. It was an official of the U.S. Office of Education who, in a report, blandly lumped together "the blind and the partially seeing, the deaf and the hard of hearing, the speech-defective, the crippled, the delicate, the epileptic, the mentally deficient, the socially maladjusted, and the extraordinarily gifted"—strange bedfellows indeed.

All this would perhaps not matter much if intelligence invariably triumphed over all obstacles, but of course it does not. Intelligence does, it is true, stand up for its rights more stubbornly than one might expect, rising above inept teachers, boring classes, and tiresome jobs. Nonetheless, an inhospitable environment can cause it serious and sometimes irreparable harm. Even a hospitable environment, for that matter, does not guarantee that the full range of a person's intelligence will be called into play. Fatigue, illness, boredom, or just plain laziness can have a considerable effect on how much one accomplishes.* So can the vagaries of the mind. James Harvey Robinson, a historian much concerned with the play and interplay of ideas, writes amusingly of the difference between Kant's "pure reason" and what actually takes place when we think: "Let us forget for the moment any impressions we may have derived from the philosophers, and see what seems to happen in ourselves. The first thing that we notice is that our thought moves with such incredible rapidity

---

* Hallowell Bowser tells the story of the Harvard student who, unable to get an assignment ready by the appointed day, explained to the professor, "I had planned to have my paper finished today but I wasn't feeling very well." "Young man," replied the professor, fixing him with an unsympathetic eye, "you will find, when you have had more experience with life, that most of the world's work is done by people who aren't feeling very well."

that it is almost impossible to arrest any specimen of it long enough to have a look at it. When we are offered a penny for our thoughts, we always find that we have recently had so many things in mind that we can easily make a selection that will not compromise us too nakedly. On inspection we shall find that even if we are not downright ashamed of a great part of our spontaneous thinking, it is far too intimate, personal, ignoble, or trivial to permit us to reveal more than a small part of it. ... We find it hard to believe that other people's thoughts are as silly as our own, but they probably are."

So far we have concerned ourselves largely with obstacles to the functioning of human intelligence: the American egalitarian tradition, with its mistrust of excessive braininess; our educational system, with its confusions in the face of unusual intelligence; and the quirky ways in which the mind itself works. Despite these obstacles and others, however, some minds manage to work wonderfully well. I am indebted to Ivan Schuller of Evanston, Illinois, for an anecdote illustrative of the mathematical mind at work. Writes Mr. Schuller:

The following question was put to the distinguished mathematician von Neumann by one of his students: Two cyclists start cycling, simultaneously, from the two ends of a 100-mile-long road.

They bicycle at a speed of forty miles per hour. At the moment they start, a fly leaves one of the bicycles and starts flying back and forth between the two cyclists until they meet. If the fly travels at 60 miles an hour, how many miles does it fly before the cyclists meet? One should not, of course, try to add up the infinite series. All you have to do is figure that the cyclists meet in an hour and a quarter and that the fly travels 75 miles in that time. When von Neumann heard the problem he instantaneously gave the right answer. His student said, "It is very strange but everybody tries to add up the infinite series." "What do you mean 'strange'?" von Neumann replied. "That's how I did it."

In my correspondence with puzzle enthusiasts I have found that though not all manifestations of genius are as celebrated as von Neumann's, they may be equally amusing. People whose names you and I have never heard of repeatedly demonstrate that they take a full measure of delight in the play of the mind. In one of my puzzle columns I described a zoo containing thirty birds and animals with a total of 100 feet and asked how many birds and how many animals there were. The answer, obtainable by the use of two simple equations, was meant to be twenty animals and ten birds, but for Nasim Ahmed of Stillwater, Oklahoma, that was too obvious (and not enough fun). His answer: thirty animals, no birds. The animals he had in mind were a centipede and twenty-nine boa constrictors.

Another correspondent cites a different question but gives an equally inventive answer. His question:

You are a captain in charge of one sergeant and four men. Your task is to raise a 100-foot flagpole, sliding it into a hole ten feet deep. You have two ropes—one 22 feet long and one 26 feet long—and two shovels and two buckets. How do you accomplish this?

My correspondent's solution: "You say, 'Sergeant, get that flagpole up.'"

Martin Antila of Bridgeport, Connecticut, also delights in the pleasures of the mind, to judge by a communication he sent me not long ago. "There are ten ravens on the roof of a house," Mr. Antila begins with perfectly straight face. "A hunter shoots one of them with his rifle. How many of the ravens are left on the roof?" Mr. Antila, proving that things are seldom what they seem, provides four alternate answers.

Answer No. 1: None, if the dead one falls off and the rest fly away.

Answer No. 2: Ten, if the roof is so flat that the dead raven doesn't fall off and the shot is fired from so far away that the rest of the ravens aren't scared away by the shot.

Answer No. 3: One, if the roof is so flat that the dead raven doesn't fall off and the shot is so loud that the live ones are frightened away.

Answer No. 4: Nine, if the roof is so steep that the dead one falls off and the shot is so quiet that the nine don't hear it and fly away.

Whatever intelligence is finally judged to be, it is certainly in some way a major component of mental gymnastics like these. It is clear, I am happy to say, that intelligence, in these delightfully playful forms, flourishes despite all the hazards and obstacles we have been discussing.

That salutary phenomenon, as we shall see, is exactly what this book is all about.

II

On logic, subways, and going forward by going sideways

One of my favorite puzzles, despite the fact that it contains a geographical wrinkle that renders it unfair under most circumstances, asks simply that you supply the next number in the series 4, 14, 23, 34, and 42. After experimenting with various intervals, fiddling with countless possible relationships, and finally discovering that the numbers apparently constitute no ordinary series, most intelligent people will find themselves turning at last to more remote possibilities. What, exactly, *are* those numbers? People's ages? House numbers? Years with some special significance? It is only at this point that the solver—provided he is familiar with the New York City subway system—is prepared to see that they are the street numbers of the stops on the Sixth Avenue and Eighth Avenue lines (and that the next stop is 50th Street).

Though that puzzle is, of course, uncommonly obscure, it illustrates an important aspect of the best of the variety of puzzle that depends primarily on logic for a solution: at first glance many of them appear to be impossible to solve. Either you don't seem to have enough information, or else they look so difficult that you imagine they would require the entire M.I.T. faculty to come up with an answer, or else some other element is maddeningly askew. The appearance of impossibility is, however, exactly what makes some puzzles so interesting. They call into play what one puzzle solver has called "a kind of sideways approach to logic that is not reducible to formula"—exactly what Arthur Koestler had in mind when he wrote, in *The Act of Creation*, about the manner in which creative people sometimes find themselves "blocked," unable to see any way to move toward a problem's solution. It is then, he writes, during this "period of incubation," that unexpected insights often come, seemingly out of nowhere.

This process applies equally well to puzzles like the ones in this chapter. Though you cannot always tell exactly where you are headed, or indeed whether you are headed anywhere at all, persistence—no matter how frustrated and seemingly purposeless—will usually yield results.

All the puzzles in this chapter, then, will give way to a properly enlightened persistence, even though that may seem unlikely when you first set eyes on them. They require no knowledge that the ordinary reader does not have. They are utterly free of trickery. There are no misleading clues, nor are there any of the other base forms of skulduggery all too often found in puzzles. Furthermore, you don't need a computer or a wastebasketful of calculations. These are, in short, exactly what they appear to be: tough, rigidly logical problems that can be solved by tough, rigidly logical thinking, properly seasoned every now and then with a bit of the aforementioned sideways approach. Two or three, for comic relief, are really quite easy.

It may be, of course, that you are one of the lucky ones who will have no need to rely on persistence. After all, a single blinding burst of intellect will do nicely, too. But isn't it good to know persistence is there to fall back on if you should need it?

1. Moving Experience

By moving only one pail, line them up so that full pails and empty ones alternate:

1   2   3   4   5   6

2. Horseplay

An aged and, it appears, somewhat eccentric king wants to pass his throne on to one of his two sons. He decrees that a horse race shall be held and that the son who owns the slower horse shall become king. The sons, each fearing that the other will cheat by having his horse go less fast than it is capable of, ask a wise man's advice. With only two words the wise man insures that the race will be fair. What does he say?

3. Troublesome Ten

How are the following numbers arranged? 0, 2, 3, 6, 7, 1, 9, 4, 5, 8.

4. Next

What are the next four numbers in this series: 12, 1, 1, 1, 2, 1, 3 . . . ,

5. Liquid Assets

A wine merchant dies, leaving his three sons seven barrels full of wine, seven barrels half full of wine, and seven empty barrels. In his will he specifies that each son shall receive exactly the same number of full, half-full, and empty barrels. Can his wish be carried out? If so, how?

6. Truth or Consequences

A smart explorer is captured by savages who order him: "Make a statement. If what you say is true, you will be hanged. If it is false, you will be shot." What does the explorer say that saves his life?

7. Cover-up

Water lilies double in area every twenty-four hours. At the beginning of the summer there is one water lily on a lake. It takes sixty days for the lake to become completely covered with water lilies. On what day is it half covered?

8. Ups and Downs

On his way to work each day, a man living on the fifteenth floor of an apartment building takes the elevator to the first floor. On his return, he takes it to the seventh floor and walks the remaining eight floors to his apartment. Why?

9. Double Cross

You want to get to a castle that is surrounded by a ten-foot moat (see diagram). You have two planks, each nine and a half feet long, but nothing to fasten them together with. How can you use the planks to reach the castle?

10. Hourglass Figures

You have two hourglasses—a four-minute glass and a seven-minute glass. You want to measure nine minutes. How do you do it?

11. The Rules

A certain bus line does not allow passengers to carry luggage over four feet long onto its buses. A man has a five-foot fishing rod. How can he take it onto a bus?

12. Double Play

Two men played checkers. They played five games and each won the same number of games. How?

13. Balancing Act

Ten bags are full of coins. All the coins look the same, but those in one of the bags weigh one gram less than those in the other nine bags. You have a scale but are permitted to make only one weighing. How do you find out which bag contains the lighter coins?

14. The Case of the Jealous Husbands

Three men, traveling with their wives, come to a river. There they find one boat that can hold only two people at a time. Since all the husbands are extremely jealous, no woman can be left with a man unless her husband is present. How do they cross the river?

15. Waiting Game

A man who enjoys watching trains likes to walk to a nearby railroad track to wait for one to go by. Each time, upon his return, he makes a note of whether the one he saw was a passenger train or a freight. Over the years, his figures show that 90 per cent of the trains have been passenger trains. One day he meets an official of the railroad and is surprised to learn that in fact passenger trains and freight trains are precisely equal in number. Why did the man, whom we may presume to have made random trips to the railroad tracks, see such a disproportionate number of passenger trains?

16. Sorting the Numbers

The numbers from 1 to 14 are divided into three groups as follows:

GROUP 1

0 3 6
8 9

GROUP 2

1 4 7
11 14

GROUP 3

2 5 10
12 13

Which groups do the next three numbers belong in?

15 16 17

17. Sleeper

A census taker asks a housewife how many people live in her house and what their ages are. The woman tells him that her three daughters live in the house, that the product of their ages is thirty-six, and that the sum of their ages is the number of the house next door. The census taker goes next door and looks at the number of the house. When he returns he tells the woman that the information she gave him is not sufficient, whereupon the woman tells him, "My oldest daughter is sleeping upstairs." The census taker thanks her and promptly figures out the daughters' ages. What are they and how does he know?

18. Price List

A woman goes into a hardware store to buy something for her house. She asks the clerk the price, and the clerk replies, "The price of one is twelve cents, the price of thirty is twenty-four cents, and the price of a hundred and forty-four is thirty-six cents." What does the woman want to buy?

19. Lucky Numbers

Two men are talking. One says to the other, "I have three sons whose ages I want you to ascertain from the following clues. Stop me when you know their ages.

"1. The sum of their ages is thirteen.

"2. The product of their ages is the same as your age.

"3. My oldest son weighs sixty-one pounds."

"Stop," says the second man. "I know their ages."

What are they?

III

Space, Grand Central Terminal, and the man who stood too close

We have all had the experience of not noticing that the air conditioning in an office building is on until it is suddenly turned off. For exactly the same reason—call it the invisibility of the familiar—we are unaware of countless things that are nonetheless of enormous importance to us. Space is a good example. Psychologists, as we have seen, have long disagreed over exactly how many individually identifiable components there are in a person's I.Q. Is it just one? Is it 120? There is practically no disagreement, however, about the fact that one of those components, no matter what the total may ultimately be determined to be, is the ability to think in spatial terms. A good sense of space is indispensable to doing well on I.Q. tests and, if such tests have any real validity, even to living and thinking successfully.

Yet few people give much thought to space or to how it impinges upon their lives. Architects do, of course. Industrial designers do. Basketball and football players, calculating their moves in millimeters, assuredly do. But most of the rest of us seldom think about it.

A pity, too. Space, as a moment's reflection will reveal, is in fact of transcendent importance in human affairs. How often have you found yourself feeling uncomfortable solely because the space in which you found yourself was ineptly designed? Compare, if you doubt the effects of space on the human spirit, two buildings, both of them designed for virtually the same purpose. On the one hand, consider Grand Central Terminal in New York City. With its towering vaults, broad corridors, and lavish decorative motifs, Grand Central proclaims the importance of the traveler. One cannot be in the station, even in the crush of rush hour, without feeling elevated, enhanced. The person who designed the station plainly felt that important things would take place in it, that important people (you and I) would pass through it. Now think of almost any contemporary airline terminal in almost any city. The airline terminal, by contrast, was built merely to process passengers—to move you through it as fast as possible, and never mind how you happen to feel about what is being done to you. The person who designed it cared about the process, not the people.

Space is not, however, just a matter of aesthetics. It can have quite practical and demonstrable consequences. Some years ago I worked with a South American writer. He was a pleasant, intelligent, and able person. He did his job well. Yet I always felt vaguely uncomfortable with him. Was it an only partly concealed aggressiveness that I sensed in him? Or something else? I did not know, and it was not until some time after he had returned to South America that I finally learned what the problem had been. In his part of the world, two people in conversation customarily stand only a foot and a half or so apart, while in the United States we stand perhaps two feet apart. The difference was enough to make me feel that he was crowding me, and it was no doubt enough to make him feel that I was being remote and standoffish.

To do well on the problems in this chapter will not necessarily help solve social problems like that one. Nor will it win you friends or otherwise improve your life. It may, in fact, do exactly the opposite, particularly if, upon discovering a puzzle you especially like, you force everyone you encounter to try it too (a malady that should perhaps be known as Fixx's syndrome). But at least you will have the satisfaction of knowing, as you work your way through them, that they are based on one of the crucial capacities of your mind.

1. Garden Spot

Plant ten trees in five rows of four trees each.

2. Pieces of Eight

Cut a cake into eight equal pieces with only three cuts.

3. Wolf Pen

Nine wolves are in a square enclosure at

the zoo. Build two more square enclosures and put each wolf in a pen by itself:

4. Counting Sheep

Sheep, on the other hand, are kept in a circular pen. Draw three lines and put each sheep in a pen by itself:

5. Outside Chance

Without lifting your pencil from the paper, join all sixteen dots with six straight lines:

6. Variation on a Variation

The problem above is a variation of the more common nine-dot problem, in which you are asked to connect the dots using four straight lines. Though most people do not at first think of going outside the confines of the dots, the puzzle is actually solved quite easily:

But can you solve it using only *three* straight lines?

7. Knowing the Angles

How many triangles can you find in this figure?

8. Playing the Angles

Divide the figure into four equal parts, each one the same size and shape:

9. Four in One

Now divide this figure into four equal parts of the same size and shape:

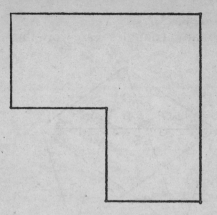

10. Keeping Up Appearances

A wooden block is cut into two pieces and reassembled so that it looks like the figure below. (The pattern looks the same on all four sides.) How is it done?

11. Square Deal

CAN YOU DRAW A PERFECT SQUARE HAVING ONE DOT ON EACH OF ITS 4 SIDES BUT NO SIDE IS TO TOUCH ANY OF THE WORDS WHICH ARE PRINTED HEREIN? IT IS NOT AS EASY AS IT MAY APPEAR AT FIRST GLANCE.

12. Once Over Lightly

Without lifting your pencil from the paper, or folding the paper, make the following figure, going over each line only once:

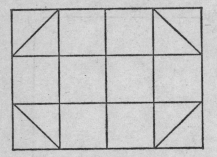

13. Cutting Up

Cut a square into four equal pieces that can be arranged to form a cross in which all sides are equal.

14. Bugged

Four bugs—A, B, C, and D—are at the corners of a ten-inch square. Simultaneously, and at a constant rate, A crawls directly toward B, B toward C, C toward D, and D toward A. How far does each bug travel before they meet?

IV

Words for the wise

When I was studying Latin in high school the teacher, Mr. Wedge, one day drew the following picture on the blackboard:

This mysterious object, he explained, had been found by archaeologists excavating the site of an ancient Roman city. What, he asked us, did we think its purpose had been? The entire class began puzzling. The inscription, whatever it was, looked vaguely like Latin, and the object certainly looked ancient enough, but no one could figure it out. Finally, Mr. Wedge showed us how to divide the letters into the proper bunches: TO TIE HORSES TO. An anguished groan went up, and I of course joined in. But that moment was the beginning of a lifelong love affair with verbal puzzles. The ones in this chapter are some of the best I have come across over the years.

1. Categories

The letters of the alphabet can be grouped into four distinct classes: The first thirteen letters establish the categories:

AM
BCDEK
FGJL
HI

Place the remaining thirteen letters in their proper categories.

2. Five in a Row

What word has five vowels in a row?

3. Spooked

What word has five consonants in a row?

4. Invitation

According to E.M. Halliday, an editor of *American Heritage*, Frederick the Great once sent the following message to Voltaire:

avec moi à

$$\frac{6}{100}$$

—and received the following reply:

$$G \, a$$

What did the exchange mean?

5. About December

This is an unusual month—Santa, snow, and so on. This is an unusual paragraph, too. How quickly can you find out what is so uncommon about it? It looks so ordinary that you may think nothing is odd about it until you match it with most paragraphs this long. If you put your mind to it and study it you will find out, but nobody may assist you; do it without any coaching. Go to work and try your skill at figuring it out. Par on it is about half an hour. Good luck—and don't blow your cool.

6. Strange

What five-letter word has only one consonant?

7. Key Question

What word contains six consonants in a row?

8. Fore and Aft

Put the same letters at the front and back of *ergro* to form a common English word.

9. Ups and Downs

What simple English statement is represented by the following?

Stand	Take	Mine	Taking
1	U	2	My

10. Vowel Play

What words contain all six vowels in order? (There are at least two of them.)

11. Repeater

What word contains the same vowel repeated six times?

12. Bad Spellers

It is said that no one in Lord Palmerston's cabinet could spell the following correctly when it was dictated to him: *It is disagreeable to witness the embarrassment of a harassed peddler gauging the symmetry of a peeled potato.* Try it on your friends and see if things have improved since Palmerston's time.

13. Fish Story

Years ago—so long ago that I no longer remember the source (was it Shaw?)—I read, in connection with the vagaries of English pronunciation, that *ghoti* can be made to spell *fish*—the *f* sound as in *enough, i* as in *women,* and *sh* as in *attention.* What, by similar (but not precisely identical) reasoning, does *iewkngheaurrhphthewempeighgh-teaps* spell?

14. The Long Way
What one-syllable word has nine letters?

15. Less Is More
What one-syllable word, when two letters are removed from it, becomes a two-syllable word?

16. Formula
What common chemical compound is represented by the following: HIJKLMNO?

17. Reckoning
Make a sentence by rearranging the following:

OOOOII248

18. Inside Stories

What English words contain the following letters consecutively and in the order given?

wsst   wkw

ycam   cheo

bpoe   erha

simmo   gnt

V

Mathematics, misery, and pure joy

Think back to your first encounter with numbers, to your earliest days of struggling with arithmetic. Do you find your mind filled with happy memories of the experience? If your school days were anything like mine, you do not. On the contrary, chances are that what you remember are hour after childhood hour of grinding travail—unendingly pointless calculations, vast tables that needed to be memorized, frustrating efforts to get an answer to come out right. Even on a first meeting, one might actually find oneself enjoying reading or geography or history. But practically no child likes arithmetic.

This is a curious phenomenon, one full of ironies, since it so frequently happens that at some time in the ensuing years mathematics turns into the purest and most joyful of recreations ("Pick a number from one to ten . . .") On the table at my side as I write this are several books: Martin Gardner's wonderful

Mathematical Carnival, Jack Frohlichstein's
Mathematical Fun, Games and Puzzles, Geoff-
rey Mott-Smith's *Mathematical Puzzles*, *The
Calculator Handbook*, by A. N. Feldzamen and
Faye Henle, and Philip Heafford's *The Math
Entertainer*. All of them—even the calculator
guide, with its chapter on "Hobbies, Recreations, and Gambling"—dwell, you will notice,
on the pleasures of mathematics. They all seem
to be saying: At times we *must* use math; these
books are for those carefree times when we
simply *want to.*

The recreational uses of math are by no
means new. Martin Gardner writes of an oc-
currence a century and a half ago in the little
town of Cabot, in the northeastern corner of
Vermont. Today Cabot is known chiefly for
the cheeses produced at its dairy co-oper-
ative, but in the early years of the nineteenth
century it was celebrated as the home of one
Zerah Colburn, a calculating prodigy who,
even before he could read and write, had
learned the multiplication table to 100.
Young Zerah performed publicly in England
when he was eight years old, multiplying two
four-digit numbers nearly as fast as any calculator can today and he even wrote an auto-
biography, *A Memoir of Zerah Colburn:
written by himself ... with his peculiar
methods of calculation.* His audiences were
so impressed that several admirers, including
Washington Irving, raised money to send
him to school in London and Paris.

Nor was Zerah Colburn by any means the first person to think of entertaining us with mathematics. Mathematical puzzles, games, and paradoxes can be traced back to the very brink of prehistory. This is really not very surprising. We take it for granted, just as soon as teachers stop rubbing our noses in numbers, that math can be wonderful fun. It is in that spirit that the puzzles in this chapter are offered. Regard them not as enemies to be swiftly bludgeoned and conquered, but as friendly companions to spend a few convivial hours with. They are certain to repay your good will.

1. Double Trouble
Arrange the numerals 1 through 9 so that, when added, they will equal 100.

2. Missing Links
Find the product of the following: (x–a) (x–b) (x–c) . . . (x–z)

3. Growing Old Together
A ship is twice as old as its boiler was when the ship was as old as the boiler is. The sum of their ages equals 49 years. How old is the ship and how old is the boiler?

4. Rope Trick

Two flagpoles are each 100 feet high. A rope 150 feet long is strung between the tops of the flagpoles. At its lowest point the rope sags to within 25 feet of the ground. How far apart are the flagpoles?

5. Animal Farm

A farmer buys 100 animals for $100. Cows are $10 each, sheep $3.00 each, and pigs 50 cents each. (Plainly, this all happened quite some time ago.) How many of each did he buy?

6. Changeless

What is the largest sum of money in current United States coins (but no silver dollars, please) that a person can have in his pocket without being able to give someone change for a dollar, half dollar, quarter, dime, or nickel?

7. The Missing Dollar

This is an old but wonderfully perplexing problem.

Three men went to a hotel and were told that there was only one room left and that it would cost $30 for the night. They paid $10 apiece and went to the room. The desk clerk, discovering that by mistake he had overcharged them by $5.00, asked the bellboy to return the $5.00. The bellboy, not being as honest as the desk clerk, reasoned that since $5.00 is not easy to divide three ways, he would keep $2.00 and return $1.00 to each of the three men. Each man thus actually paid only $9.00 apiece, or a total of $27 for the room. Add to that the $2.00 the bellboy kept and the total is $29. Where did the missing dollar go?

8. The Hard Way

Without changing the order of these digits, place the fewest possible mathematical symbols between them in order to make the equation true: 1 2 3 4 5 6 7 8 9 = 100. It can, of course, be done quite easily by using a "not equals" sign ($\neq$), but that would be taking the easy way out, wouldn't it?

9. Match Trick

Can you make the equation true by moving only one match?

$$ I\,I = VI $$

10. Where There's a Will

A Middle Eastern potentate died, leaving 17 camels. His will specified that they be divided among his three sons as follows:

1/2 to the oldest son

1/3 to the second son

1/9 to the youngest son

The three sons were puzzling over how this could be done when a wise man happened to ride by on a camel. How did the wise man solve their problem?

11. X Marks the Spot

Solve for X:

$$ \sqrt{X + \sqrt{X + \sqrt{X\ldots}}} = 2 $$

12. Time Out

A customer gives a $20 bill to a jeweler for a watch priced at $12. Because he is short of change, the jeweler changes the $20 bill at a store next door. He gives the watch and $8.00 to the customer. Later the neighboring storekeeper, discovering the $20 bill to be counterfeit, returns it to the jeweler, who exchanges it for a genuine $20 bill. If the jeweler had a 100 per cent markup on the watch, how much did he actually lose in the transaction?

13. Burned Up

How many cigars can a hobo make from twenty-five cigar butts if he needs five butts to make one cigar?

14. Up a Tree

If John gives Paul one apple, they will have the same number of apples. If Paul gives John one, John will have twice as many as Paul has. How many apples does each have?

15. It All Adds Up

Arrange eight 8s so that when added they will equal 1,000.

16. Line-up

By drawing one line, make the following figure into an even number (without violating numerical convention):

$$\text{I} \times$$

VI

Disturbers of
the puzzler's peace

Lest I be suspected of a penchant for under-handedness that I do not, so far as I know, even remotely possess, let me say at once that, of all the chapters in this book, this is the one I like least. (It is not without significance that it is among the shortest.) In my earliest ruminations, in fact, I did not even plan to include it, not through oversight but because the sorts of puzzles found here seem to me uncomfortably close to shaggydog stories, to be greeted not with appreciation but with groans.

There are I know, plenty of people who dearly love puzzles that inflict an intellectual whiplash. My daughter Betsy, thirteen years old and not at all reluctant to outwit her elders when she can, is an excellent example. I had long ago encountered, as you no doubt have, the familiar bus driver puzzle. It goes: "You're driving a bus. At the first stop two passengers get on. At the next, seven passengers get on and one gets off . . ." and so on through a dozen of more stops, until you are ultimately flattened by the disarming question: "How many times did the bus stop?" So I was ready, or at least thought I was, when Betsy began to recite the coming and goings of the bus passengers—ready, indeed, for anything, for I was cannily counting both the stops *and* the passengers. But what I was not ready for, as Betsy was pretty sure I would not be, was what turned out to be her question, "How old was the bus driver?" (Nor was I able, by that time, to remember that she had begun by saying, *"You're* driving a bus . . .")

Despite such firsthand evidence of the popularity of this kind of puzzle, I nonetheless did not, as I say, intend to include any in this book. Its predecessor, *Games for the Superintelligent*, gained whatever freedom from impurity it had from the fact that its puzzles, despite their other flaws and shortcomings, were all impeccably straightforward and could be solved, each and every one of them, by nothing trickier than a rigorous application of logic. You didn't have to wonder if the author was trying to outwit you—he wasn't—and readers, to judge by the evidence that reached me, welcomed the certainty that what they had to deal with were merely the puzzles themselves and not a syntactical mine field.

All this sounds, four years after the fact, impressively farsighted. In truth it was nothing of the sort. I simply included the kinds of puzzles that give me special delight, and it was only luck that there proved to be a lot of other people who like the same kind of puzzle. Nevertheless, as I talked with puzzle aficionados I became increasingly aware that there are plenty of them who are not the least bit like me: they genuinely like—nay, *crave*—tricks, the trickier the better. Then, as I went through my files in preparation for compiling this book, I was struck by how many people—scores of them, in fact—had sent me puzzles that deliberately set out to deceive. I was also struck, though it took me a long time to admit it, even to myself, by the fact that despite my better instincts I found some of them wonderfully amusing.

And so it was that I determined to include a sampling in this volume. My first thought was to seed them subversively through the entire book, popping them in at odd, unsuspected moments like tacks in a driveway. But that would have rendered all the puzzles suspect. A reader would never have been able to tell whether he was faced with a genuine puzzle or some bit of sleight of hand. No, it was better, even at the risk of giving too obvious a warning blast, to banish the whiplash puzzles to their own preserve, like so many dangerous animals. And that is precisely what, for better or worse, this chapter is all about.

1. Where There's Smoke

If you had only one match and entered a room in which there were a kerosene lamp, a fireplace, and a wood-burning stove, which should you light first?

2. Last Wrongs

Can a man living in Chapel Hill, North Carolina, be buried west of the Mississippi?

3. Look Again

There is three errers in this sentence. Can you find them?

4. Coin Trick

You have thirty-five cents in two coins.

One of them is not a quarter. what are the coins?

5. Over and Out
Construct this figure without lifting your pencil from the surface of the paper and without traversing any line more than once:

6. So You Think You Know the Law
Is it legal in South Dakota for a man to marry his widow's sister?

7. Holiday
Do they have a Fourth of July in England?

8. Disaster
If a plane crashes directly on the line between two states, where are the survivors buried?

9. Voyager
How many animals of each species did Moses take aboard the ark with him?

10. Kaffeeklatsch
You have three cups of coffee and fourteen lumps of sugar. Sweeten all three cups using an odd number of lumps in each one. (You must use all the lumps.)

11. Days Off
Some months have thirty days. Some have thirty-one. How many months have twenty-eight days?

12. Cannonball
An electric train heads north at eighty miles an hour. The wind is blowing from the east at twenty miles an hour. In what direction will the smoke from the engine point?

13. In the Groove

How many grooves does the average twelve-inch 33 1/3 LP record have?

VII

The damnable dozen

This chapter is a sort of bonus or dividend. It consists of the dozen puzzles that readers of this book's predecessor have found most interesting or, in one or two cases, most maddeningly difficult. Even if you have already worked them out, they are such an intricate set of puzzles, so logical, precise, and demanding, that some of them may well reward a second attempt. If you didn't work them earlier (or couldn't), their rewards still await you.

When *Games for the Superintelligent* first appeared back in 1972, I had, I confess, no very clear idea of which puzzles were going to prove most appealing to readers. I had had scant experience with people who, like myself, find a good puzzle as refreshing as a cold beer on an August day. In preparing *GFTS* I corresponded, it is true, with scores of puzzlers but by its very nature it was a pretty single-minded correspondence—this puzzle, that solution—and I was not able to arrive at any steady sense of what kind of people they were or what kind of puzzles they were going to like most when they finally laid eyes on the whole supermarketful.

Perhaps the strongest clue I had was one that came to me when I first encountered a few members of Mensa, the high-I.Q. society. I was writing a magazine article about the organization and I visited a Mensa meeting at a Manhattan hotel. There was a speaker (whose name and topic I no longer remember), and there was a lot of spirited and occasionally intense debate among the members, suggesting that enormous, even if not readily apparent, issues were being argued. When the formal part of the meeting was over, a half dozen Mensa members went to a restaurant downstairs for more conversation. I joined them. Even before food and drink had been ordered, a glowingly lovely young woman produced a pencil and, like one hot on the scent of the Grail, began scribbling puzzles on our napkins. Occasionally, as the hours wore on, someone would make a move to ease her away from her obsession but the young woman was not to be stopped. Puzzles were her thing, and so long as she was present they were going to be ours too. She kept us at it until, in self-defense, we finally had to excuse ourselves and wander off into the night like so many victims of sensory overload or oriental brainwash.

That lovely and forceful young woman

was often in my thoughts as I wrote *GFTS* Were there more out there like her? I did not know. Was she typical of the people who like puzzles? Again, I had no way of knowing. I could not quite believe there could be that many true believers, but on the other hand I had no evidence that there were not. In short, I didn't have any idea at all what kind of people I was writing the book for.

As anyone will do when he doesn't know what he's doing, I hedged my bets. I threw in every kind of puzzle I could find—a crossword puzzle, a cross-*number* puzzle (a truly noxious variant of the crossword), some of the strangest word games ever conceived by the mind of man, and even a few things to amuse the kids with on automobile trips. I was like a nervous cowboy expecting an ambush: I didn't know which canyon the bad guys were going to come through, so I tried to cover them all.

I needn't have worried. Readers, as it turned out, were not at all reluctant to let me know what they liked. In the four years since *GFTS* fiirst appeared, several hundred of them have written me to express their opinions of the book, paragraph by paragraph, and very few puzzles, you may be sure, have been overlooked in this sometimes exhilarating, sometimes humbling process. A number of readers have troubled to telephone me, some of them insomniac souls who have sought to mend my ways by instructing me while I tried to sleep. Still others have expressed their views, both for good and for ill, to the publisher.

It is quite clear that most readers like exactly the kind of puzzles I like—strenuously logical ones that require, in most cases, a certain flash of insight before they can be solved. I am surprised, in fact, that no reader has ever complained to me that a puzzle was too tough or required too much time. In fact, people invariably like the tough ones especially well, and they particularly like those—No. 1, below, is a good example—that look at first glance as if there could be no possible way to solve them.

The twelve puzzles that follow proved to be the cream of the crop. The final one, incidentally, is one of those I first heard from the lovely Mensa member in the hotel restaurant. Perhaps because she smiled at me so winningly as she wrote it on my napkin, it has been one of my favorites ever since.

1. No Peeking
Three boxes are labeled "Apples," "Oranges," and "Apples and Oranges." Each label is incorrect. You may select only one fruit from one box. (No feeling around or peeking permitted.) How can you label each box correctly?

2. Similarities

What do the following words have in common: *deft, first, calmness, canopy, laughing, stupid, crabcake, hijack?*

3. Question

A traveler comes to a fork in the road and does not know which way to go to reach his destination. There are two men at the fork, one of whom always lies while the other always tells the truth. The traveler doesn't know which is which. He may ask one of the men only one question to find his way. What is his question and which man does he ask?

4. Alice Did It

Punctuate the following so it makes sense: *Alice while Matthew had had had had had had had had had had had a better effect on the teacher.*

5. The Spider and the Fly

A 12×30 foot room has a 12-foot ceiling. In the middle of the end wall, a foot above the floor, is a spider. The spider wants to capture a fly in the middle of the opposite wall, one foot below the ceiling. What is the shortest path the spider can take?

6. Checkmate

A standard chessboard is truncated by removing corner squares diagonally opposite each other:

Can thirty-one dominoes, each able to cover two adjacent squares, be used to cover all sixty-two squares of the truncated chessboard? If so, how? If not, why not?

7. Case of the Counterfeit Coin

You have twelve identical-looking coins, one of which is counterfeit. The counterfeit coin is either heavier or lighter than the rest. The only scale available is a simple balance. Using the scale only three times, find the counterfelt coin.

8. True or False?

A missionary visits an island where two
tribes live. One tribe always tells the truth.
The other always lies. The truth-tellers live
on the western side of the island and the liars
live on the eastern side. The missionary's
problem is to determine who tells the truth
by asking one native only one question.

The missionary, seeing a native walking in
the distance, asks a nearby native: "Go ask
that native in the distance which side of the
island he lives on." When the messenger returns he answers: "He says he lives on the
western side." Is the messenger a truthteller
or a liar? How can you be sure?

9. Taking Sides

Given: Four pieces of cardboard. You are
told that each one is either red or green on
one side, and that each one has either a circle
or a square on the other side. They appear on
the table as follows:

Which ones must you pick up and turn over in order to have enough information to answer the question: Does every red one have a square on its other side?

10. Theirs the Reason Why

Three intelligent men, applying for a job, seem equal in all pertinent attributes, so the prospective employer, also an intelligent man, sets a simple problem for them. The job, he says, will go to the first applicant to solve it. A mark is placed on each man's forehead. The three are told that each has either a black mark or a white mark and each is to raise his hand if he sees a black mark on the forehead of either of the other two. The first one to tell what color he has and how he arrived at his answer will get the job. Each man raises his hand, and after a few seconds one man comes up with the answer. What color is his mark, and how did he figure it out?

11. Rugged Challenge

You have a 9×12-foot rug with an 8×1-foot hole in the middle. Cut the rug into two pieces (no more and no less) so that the two pieces can be sewn together to make a solid 10×10-foot rug.

12. Multiplying by 4

Supply a digit for each letter so that the equation is correct. A given letter always represents the same digit:

$$
\begin{array}{r}
A\,B\,C\,D\,E \\
\times 4 \\
\hline
E\,D\,C\,B\,A
\end{array}
$$

VIII

Solving puzzles
the superintelligent way

As we saw in Chapter 1, the minds of bright people are significantly different—in as many as 120 ways, some say—from those of their less intelligent brethren. This is as true in solving puzzles as it is in trying to live a rational life. While the ordinary mind is likely to be stubbornly trying a single fruitless assault on a problem, the gifted mind is quickly sweeping through a range of choices and winnowing the most promising methods from the many that occur to it. Then, if those methods fail, rather than giving up in discouragement it moves on to what at first seemed the less likely routes, until at length it arrives at a solution.

It is exactly as if the bright person were a miniature think tank. Instead, however, of being free to assign a separate task force to each aspect of a problem, as Herman Kahn or the Pentagon can, there is only one person to assign to all aspects. And instead of being able to study every facet of a problem simultaneously, the bright person must study them one at a time. This method is a lot slower, but it often works just as well. The chief reason for its success is that the bright person is likely to be relatively indefatigable. (Remember one of Sir Francis Galton's components of intelligence: "power of work.") While the less intelligent person, unsure of ever being able to solve a problem at all, is easily discouraged, the intelligent person is fairly sure of succeeding and therefore presses on, discouragements be damned.

Because the difference between the two types of mind depends so much upon their differing power of work, it is often difficult if not impossible to demonstrate in detail how the action of one differs from that of the other. It is, moreover, obvious that many of the things that only exceptionally intelligent minds can *do* can be readily *understood* by considerably less intelligent minds. We do not have to be geniuses ourselves to appreciate Shakespeare or understand Newton's laws of motion. It is, in fact, uncommon for someone to make so spectacularly brilliant an intellectual leap that we can only stand in awe. Most of the time we can, if we wish, tell ourselves: Why, I could easily have done that if it had only occurred to me to! (We do not dwell on the fact that it simply did *not* occur to us to.)

Despite the difficulty of showing, clearly

and without ambiguity, the characteristic ways in which bright people solve problems, their methods can at least be suggested by pointing to specific examples. To this end, let us dissect in some detail a few of the puzzles in this book.

Chapter II, Puzzle 3: At first glance this question seems to be based on a quite ordinary series of numbers, 0, 2, 3, 6, 7, 1, 9, 4, 5, 8. The series is much like the ones we have encountered all our lives. For this reason the solver, no matter what his intelligence, will most likely start by treating it in the customary way. He will examine the intervals between numbers, check to see whether any patterns repeat themselves, and, as those attempts fail, make other efforts of increasing complexity. At this point, all his efforts having come to nothing, the person of ordinary intelligence may well feel the first twinges of discouragement. Does solving the puzzle rely, perhaps, on some mathematical technique or formula he does not know? The superintelligent solver, by contrast, has a secret weapon: he knows that the puzzle, by virtue of being in this book, is likely to have a bit of English on it. He therefore veers sharply, abandons the fairly unimaginative course he has been following (with, however, the idea that he may have to return to it later), and begins looking for some totally different line of attack. Now, although he does not yet know it, he is on the right track at last. He decides, experimentally, to treat the numbers not as numbers at all but as objects. What about their shapes—their curves, straight lines, combination of curves and straight lines, and so forth? No solution presenting itself, he moves on. What about treating the numbers as words—*zero, two, three, six, seven* . . . etc.? He counts their letters, checks them for patterns, repetitions. Finding nothing there, he moves, finally, to the first letters of the words: *z, t, t, s, s, o, n, f, f, e.* Before he even has the ten letters down on paper that *z* gives it all away: The numbers are, of course, in reverse alphabetical order.

Principle 1: Consider the context of a puzzle first.

Chapter II, Puzzle 10: You are asked to use two hourglasses, a four-minute glass and a seven-minute glass, to measure out nine minutes. It requires only a moment's reflection to realize that seven and four, no matter how they may be arranged, cannot be made to add up to nine. Where, then, do we go from here? The person of ordinary intelligence is unlikely to go much of anywhere. Or perhaps he gets a bit further when an analogy occurs to him: he thinks of those puzzles about cooks who want to measure a certain amount of, say, sugar but have measuring cups of the wrong size. This line of speculation leads to a dead end, for time as measured by hourglasses cannot be subtracted in the way sugar in a measuring cup can. Time flows on and is gone; one cannot (alas!) return to some previous time, as one can pour out a bit of sugar and thereby have less. It is at this point that the superintelligent person decides to try something else. But what else is there to try? An hourglass is either running or it is not running, and no combination of running and stopped hourglasses can possibly yield nine minutes. Or can it? What about stopping one of the hourglasses in mid-run and then, if need be, restarting it? With that insight, the solution is close at hand. The solver's whole difficulty, incidentally, arises from the assumption that sand in an hourglass must be allowed to run all the way through. That, of course, is what usually happens, but there is no law saying it must always happen that way.

Principle 2: Look for uncommon ways of using a puzzle's components.

Chapter II, Puzzle 19: This is one of my favorite puzzles. A reader sent it to me in a letter, and something about his tone impressed and reassured me. I felt certain he wasn't trying to trick me but that the puzzle was honest and would reward my efforts. It did. I worked it in two sessions, the first a brief one of terrible frustration in which I was especially puzzled by the seeming irrelevance of the son's weight and by the fact, with respect to Clue No. 2, that I didn't *know* what the man's age was. How could an answer possibly be put together from such meager information? I was helpless. I stopped, went outdoors, pruned a rosebush or two. When I came back to the puzzle I had fresh determination. Suddenly it occurred to me that the weight might well be irrelevant and that the clue must be telling me something else—that there is only one oldest son, not two of the same age. It then occurred to me that it might be worth while to jot down the various combinations of ages that could satisfy the problem, so I started: 11, 1, 1; 10, 1, 2 . . . and so forth. There were fourteen of them. A moment's study revealed that two of the combinations yielded the same product: 36. Here, then, was the solution! If the answer were not one of the combinations that yield 36, the man would have known the correct combination after hearing Clue No. 2. The fact that he did not demonstrates that there was still a question in his mind, a question that was finally resolved with Clue No. 3. There is another little secret to solving this puzzle, and if it had occurred to me earlier I could have worked it in a tenth the time: the fact that you and I don't know the man's age doesn't mean that *he* doesn't know it. Of course he knows it, and that is the key to solving this puzzle.

Principle 3: If logic and persistence don't yield an answer, go out and smell the roses for a while.

Chapter III, Puzzle 1: At first glance it appears that this puzzle is simply impossible to solve. Five rows of four trees each adds up, after all, to twenty trees, or so it appears. Even allowing for the use of a few trees in more than one row, it seems exceedingly unlikely that the number of trees required can be reduced to a mere ten. Then, however, the principle becomes clear: it is necessary to plant the trees as densely as possible, making each tree serve in as many rows as possible. Diagram after diagram is tried; none works—not at first anyway. But then, sooner or later, the wondrous symmetry of nature and mathematics asserts itself and there it is, that simple and elegant answer: a star.

Principle 4: Keep at it.

Chapter III, Puzzle 2: You are asked to cut a cake into eight equal pieces with only three cuts. Any three cuts made vertically will, it is apparent, yield six pieces at most. Two cuts made vertically and a third cut made along a radius will yield only five pieces. Three cuts that fail to intersect will yield only four pieces. Things seem to be getting not better but worse! At this point the person of ordinary intelligence is likely to imagine that he is faced with something as clearly impossible as trying to separate two interlocking rings; mathematically, it simply can't be done. But it is precisely here that the superintelligent puzzle solver begins to rise to the challenge. He looks first at the components of the puzzle: (1) a cake and (2) a knife for cutting it into those elusive eight pieces. He reminds himself that the puzzle can, after all, be solved; it would not be in this book if it could not (see Principle 1 above). Furthermore, he knows there is nothing tricky or misleading about the question. (He has been assured that all the tricky questions have been sequestered in Chapter VI.) So he knows it is worth his while to treat the puzzle in a straightforward way—he need not suspect an ambush. He is, at the same time, certain by now that it cannot be solved by making three cuts of the kind we customarily make in cakes. Well, what other kinds are there? A rough sort of answer comes to him at once; vertical cuts, horizontal cuts, cuts taking various improbable directions through the cake. It is a matter of only a few moments before he sees that two vertical cuts, at right angles to each other, and one horizontal cut will do the trick neatly.

Principle 5: If something has always been done one way, look for another way.

Chapter III, Puzzle 5: In this one you are asked to join sixteen dots with six straight lines without lifting your pencil from the paper. Any puzzler, no matter what his intelligence, will no doubt find a pencil and start fiddling. (It always makes sense to get a quick view of the magnitude of things.) In a short time it will be clear that this one isn't going to be easy; there always seem to be too many dots and two few lines. If you are knowledgeable about puzzles, you will recall that in some problems of this general type the solution can be reached only by resorting to extraordinary measures—folding the paper, for example, or piercing it with a pencil point and letting a line snake its way through the hole from one side to the other. But there is nothing in the language of this puzzle to suggest that such lawbreaking is called for. Furthermore, solutions based on such methods would unquestionably constitute trickery, wouldn't they? (There will be time enough later, if things start to go really badly, to ask if we are being tricked.) For the time being, better to treat it as a straightforward question, neither more nor less complex than it seems to be. What, therefore, can we do that we aren't now doing? Practically anyone, regardless of his intelligence, will no doubt

101

stumble onto the answer sooner or later, but the superintelligent, having got this far, will probably find it almost immediately. (Mental quickness, psychologists agree, is an important component of brightness.) The reason is that it will probably occur to him to ask himself whether he is by chance working under some unnecessary restriction. Of course he is—no one told him that he had to stay within the imaginary boundary of the square created by the sixteen dots!

Principle 6: Work only within those restrictions that are explicitly stated. All others are irrelevant.

Chapter IV, Puzzle 1: This puzzle is both difficult and simple. The difficulty arises from the fact that we are thoroughly conditioned to think of letters as *letters* and not as objects. A, for example, is the first letter of the alphabet. It is a vowel, too. Those things are uppermost in our minds. Only rarely do we think of A as a shape, pointed at the top like, appropriately enough, an A-frame house, with a supporting girder running horizontally to keep it from spreading out and collapsing in a most unvowellike heap. Once we have managed to bring ourselves to look at A (and at the other letters) in that way, the rest is easy.

Principle 7: Don't get tripped up by

unexpressed hypotheses. Examine all the alternatives.

Chapter V, Puzzle 2: To find the product of the series $(x-a)$ $(x-b)$ $(x-c)$ ...$(x-z)$ appears to be, as anyone can instantly see, a problem of unusual complexity for a book like this. The first reaction of the intelligent puzzle solver is therefore surprise. What is a puzzle like that doing here? It cannot even be solved with the use of a pocket calculator—not, anyway, by any method known to a mathematical layman. More and more, as one looks at it, it begins to look like something you might find on a blackboard at the Institute for Advanced Studies, being studied by a committee of bearded mathematicians, their brows furrowed in puzzlement. At this point, the intelligent solver may begin to suspect that only one reaction is really appropriate: laughter. It is, after all, ridiculous to suppose that a problem as difficult as all that would be in this book. But what to do about it? It is one thing to know that one's leg is being pulled and quite another to find out who or what is pulling it. Where, exactly, is the clue to the mystery? Well, perhaps we are making some assumption that we ought not to make (see Principle 4). What about that ellipsis (. . .), that unobtrusive mathematical symbol for *et cetera*? Ever since we first studied algebra in school, we have been seeing and using those harmless little dots; never have they concealed anything more surprising than an orderly and continuous series. What, however, lies within these particular three dots? Now, at last, we are on the track. As we start working our way through the unexpressed elements of the equation— (x–d), (x–e), and so forth—it occurs to us that eventually we will come to (x–x). Because (x–x) equals zero, the rest of the equation, no matter how tangled and mathematically variegated it is, will of course equal zero!

Principle 8: If you can't find the solution by looking at the forest, look at the trees.

Chapter V, Puzzle 5: This puzzle is difficult only if the flagpoles are not right together. If they are, as we have seen, it is absurdly simple. An extremely bright person, noticing this, decides to take a moment to see if, by chance, they *are* right together. If they are not, only a few moments have been lost. If they are, much has been gained. The bright person is not afraid to digress, to risk a small loss for a potentially large gain.

Principle 9: When you're watching a magician, don't concentrate only on the rabbit. Something important may be going on somewhere else.

Chapter V, Puzzle 16: You are given the Roman numerals representing 9—that is,

IX—and asked to change them into an even number between five and ten by adding only one line. The problem appears to have no solution. One line, after all, is simply I, and that gets us nowhere. Aha! But no one said it had to be a straight line. Could the line possibly be a bent one—V? That could give us VIX, or four, but four does not qualify since it is not between five and ten. (It could also give us IVX, or six, but the unconventional notation rules out that solution.) There seems, then, to be no way to solve this one, so long as we treat IX as Roman numerals. What else could they be, then? Well, for one thing, as the superintelligent person quickly sees, they could be treated simply as ordinary letters—a capital *i* and a capital *x*. What single line, added to *i* and *x*, might turn those letters into a word representing an even number between five and ten? From here on it's all downhill: simply note what letters of the alphabet can be formed with a single line—it is surprising how many there are—and try adding them to *i* and *x*. It will not be long before *six* turns up.

Principle 10: Assume that nothing is what it seems to be. Now, armed with this ten-point puzzle-solving arsenal, go back to Chapters II through VII and try some of the questions you found too tough the first time through.

See? Aren't you doing better already?

IX

Rating your intelligence

Let us suppose that thus far in your life you have been a mere dabbler in matters superintelligent. Now you would like to become a certified member of the superintelligentsia. There are many methods. Only one of them, however, has genuine style, and that is to think your way into Mensa, the international society for people with extraordinarily high I.Q.s. To qualify for membership you need an I.Q. in the top 2 per cent of the population. That's 133 on the Stanford-Binet test, 130 on the Wechsler Adult test, a combined score of 1,300 on the College Entrance Examination Board aptitude tests, 140 on the Army General Classification Test and 70 on the Navy General Classification Test. Once a member, you're able to attend meetings (Mensa has more than 125 chapters in the United States and a good many abroad, particularly in England and Canada), join groups with special interests ranging from parapsychology to gourmet cooking, serve as a subject in psychological studies, and participate in some of the headiest conversation to be found anywhere.

What are a person's chances of qualifying? Not as remote as you might think, especially for anyone reading this book. Two per cent works out, after all, to one in every fifty people, so a good many of those you run into each day could become members if they wanted to. And if, by chance, you spend a lot of time with people who work with their brains (college professors, let's say, or engineers or lawyers or doctors), then the proportion is no doubt considerably higher.

To help determine the likelihood of your being Mensa material yourself, the organization's psychologist, Max L. Fogel, has prepared a special test. It is published here for the first time.

The instructions are simple: Work as hard as you can for no more than forty-five minutes, then stop. A key for scoring appears on page 101. If you finish in less than forty minutes, give yourself a one-point bonus; in less than thirty-five minutes, a two-point bonus; in less than thirty minutes, a three-point bonus.*

Now, get your watch and pencils ready.

All set?

Turn the page and begin.

---

* If you are encouraged by your performance and would like to take Mensa's official preliminary test, write to Department J, Suite 1R, 1701 West Third Street, Brooklyn, N.Y. 11223. Or, if you're able to submit evidence of having attained the required score in one of the other tests cited, you can join without further testing.

1. Which figure in the bottom row should appear next in the top row?

2. Which figure in the bottom row should appear next in the top row?

3. Which figure in the bottom row should appear next in the top row?

(a)　　　(b)　　　(c)　　　(d)

4. Which figure in the bottom row should appear next in the top row?

(a)　　　(b)　　　(c)　　　(d)

5. Which figure in the bottom row should appear next in the top row?

6. "Don't throw good money after bad" means:

(*a*) Take your loss and walk away from it.

(*b*) Don't gamble; think of the future.

(*c*) Don't invest in a losing proposition.

(*d*) Don't keep gambling when you're losing.

7. The proverb "All that glisters is not gold" means:

(*a*) Fool's gold looks like gold.

(*b*) Don't be tempted by false praise.

(*c*) She may not be as adorable as she looks.

(*d*) Superficial relationships can be enjoyable, too.

8. What word means the same as the left-hand word in one sense and the same as the right-hand word in another sense?

pay——bottom

No longer applicable!

9. Love is to—— as sex is to——.

(*a*) woman; man
(*b*) cherish; caress
(*c*) enjoy; tolerate
(*d*) obey; liberate

10. What number comes next in the following series?

9, 12, 21, 48
(*a*) 69; (*b*) 70; (*c*) 129; (*d*) 144

11. Most readers of this book are sexy. All readers of this book are superintelligent. Therefore:

(*a*) Sexy readers of this book are also superintelligent.

(*b*) Sex and superintelligence don't mix well.

(*c*) All superintelligent readers of this book are sexy.

(*d*) Most readers of this book are superintelligent about sex.

12. Statistics indicate that men drivers are involved in more accidents than women drivers. It may be concluded that:

(*a*) As usual, male chauvinists are wrong about women's abilities.

(*b*) Men are actually better drivers but drive more frequently.

(*c*) Men and women drive equally well but men log more total mileage.

(*d*) Most truck drivers are men.

(*e*) Sufficient information is not available to justify a conclusion.

13. Which country does not belong:

(*a*) Canada; (*b*) Czechoslovakia; (*c*) Chile; (*d*) Iran; (*e*) Mexico; (*f*) Rumania; (*g*) the Soviet Union; (*h*) The United States; (*i*) Venezuela

14. Which word does not belong?

(*a*) bourbon; (*b*) Burgundy; (*c*) Chablis; (*d*) port; (*e*) sherry; (*f*) zinfandel

15. The floor space of a large restaurant is divided into four main dining areas. Half of the main dining areas contain two smaller dining rooms each and the other half contain four smaller dining rooms each. Ten diners can be served in each of half of the total number of rooms; fifteen can be served in each of the remaining half. What is the maximum number of diners that can be served at the same time?

(*a*) 100; (*b*) 125; (*c*) 150; (*d*) 175

16.

(a) +, —, 0; (b) 0, +, —; (c) —, +, 0; (d) 0, —, +

17. How many squares are shown below? (You may ignore any lines that pass through a square.)

(a) 19; (b) 20; (c) 21; (d) 22; (e) 23

18. A horse is most like a:

(a) camel; (b) car; (c) cow; (d) dog; (e) motorcycle

19. F is to L as B is to:

    (*a*) D; (*b*) G; (*c*) M; (*d*)T

20. Which figure in the bottom row should appear next in the top row?

    (a)   (b)   (c)   (d)

21. Barbara, Betty, and Joy own a total of eighty dresses. If half of Barbara's equals the sum of two thirds of Betty's and one fourth of Joy's, how many dresses does each own?

22. Bucky, Stephen, Tom, and Vic are weight lifters. Vic can outlift Tom but Stephen can outlift Vic. Tom can outlift Bucky but Stephen can outlift Tom. Therefore:

    (*a*) Both Bucky and Stephen can outlift Vic.

(*b*) Vic can outlift Bucky but can't outlift Tom.

(*c*) Vic can outlift Bucky by more than he can outlift Tom.

(*d*) None of the above.

23. If an airplane travels at an average speed of 500 miles per hour, how long will it take to complete twenty trips, of which five are for 1,000 miles, five for 1,500 miles, five for 2,000 miles, and five for 3,000 miles?

(*a*) 2 days and 18 hours

(*b*) 2 days and 21 hours

(*c*) 3 days

(*d*) 3 days and 3 hours

24. What number comes next in the following series?

9, 5, 8, 14, 10, 13

(*a*) 7; (*b*) 9; (*c*) 16; (*d*) 19; (*e*) 23

25. If $A \times B = 24$, $C \times D = 32$, $B \times D = 48$, and $B \times C = 24$ what does $A \times B \times C \times D$ equal?

(*a*) 480; (*b*) 576; (*c*) 744; (*d*) 768; (*e*) 824

More helpers

In the nature of things, any collection of mental recreations must be a collaborative effort. A good many of the puzzles and games in this book have been making the rounds for years, occasionally surfacing in print but often simply passing informally from hand to hand when puzzle lovers meet. For this reason there is nowhere the author of a book like this can go to do his research, no library or central repository of what he is looking for. He must depend almost entirely on the help and generosity of others who share his enthusiasms.

In this respect I have been lucky. Over the past several years scores of correspondents have written to me about puzzles. Some of the puzzles have been new to me, while others have been old ones that I might easily have overlooked had I not been reminded of them. In addition, friends, colleagues, and even a few chance acquaintances have offered ideas and given encouragement when it counted.

Among the various partners in this enterprise are:

Nasim Ahmed, Janice H. Anderson, Martin Antila, Rito Avalos, Frances H. Bentley, Stephen Bepko, Gila Berkowitz, Henry M. Black, Richard M. Block, Ron E. Breland, Maxey Brooke, Bruce Brown, Virginia H. Burney, Mike Buttke, S. Chandrashekara, Kuang-Yeh Chang, Inge Denny, Richard J. Deye, Don Dolezalek, Joseph Drago, Patricia Driskill, Neil E. Duncliffe, Charles W. Dunn, Donald W. Eckrich, Jon Erickson, Clifford J. Falk, Harry Famely, Chris Fisher, Ellen M. Fitzgerald, Max L. Fogel, Donald R. Fosnacht, Richard Gardiner, Jonathan Gerson, Todd Glasford, Jitendra Singh Goela, Anil Goyal, Dale Green, Martin B. Green, Jonathan Groner, Barbara C. Heller, William H. Hernandez, Wolfgang S. Homburger, Pyke Johnson, Jr., Martin J. Kelinsky, Frederick F. Kleinman, Marshall Kurtz, Bruce Kutner, Peter J. Lardieri, Barbara Holtz Levine, Bernard Lewis, Dave Lewis, Geraldine McDaniel, Barbara McKenzie, Raymond J. Martin, Jr., Ann Meadow, Jeffrey R. Miller, John D. Miller, Nancy A. Mitchell, Karen Montgomery, Russell A. Nahigian, Bob Nathan, C. A. Nicolaides, Gary A. Nielsen, Robert F. Oldani, Francis P. Pandolfi, Chris Peters, Joe Poindexter, Edward Purcell, Cal L. Raup, Alvin Reinstein, Steve Ross, T. M.

Rostker, D. P. Rougon, Tom Saile, Wolfgang Sannwald, Lee W. Sauer, Jeffry N. Savitz, Ivan Schuller, W. R. Sears, Nicholas Sellers, Fred U. Senfert, Manu Seth, Zach Sklar, Nguyen Thao, Don W. Tope, Elliott J. Tuckel, Jay Valancy, J. A. Washam, Joel R. Weiss, Charles Weissglass, Steve Whipple, C. A. Wiken, Larry Wizenberg, Catherine Woytko, L. Y. Wu, and, as always, the little old lady on Rose Street.

Answers to puzzles

CHAPTER II

1. Pour pail No. 2 into pail No. 5.

2. "Switch horses."

3. In reverse alphabetical order.

4. 1, 4, 1, 5, etc. The numbers represent the chimes of a clock that strikes once on the half hour.

5. Yes. Pour four of the half-full barrels together to make two more full ones. Now there are nine full barrels, three half-full barrels, and nine empty barrels. All can be divided by three.

6. He says, "I will be shot." If this were true, he would, under the terms of his sentence, be hanged. That would be contradictory. If it were false he would be shot—also contradictory. The savages are forced to release the explorer. (So he hopes, anyhow.)

7. The fifty-ninth day.

8. He is a midget and can't reach higher than the seventh-floor button.

9. Simply lay one of the planks diagonally across the edge and the other from that plank to the castle:

10. Start both hourglasses. When the four-minute glass runs out, turn it over (four minutes elapsed). When the seven-minute glass runs out, turn it over (seven minutes elapsed). When the four-minute glass runs out this time (eight minutes elapsed), the seven-minute glass has been running for one minute. Turn it over once again. When it stops, nine minutes have elapsed.

11. Make a package as shown:

12. They weren't playing each other.

13. Number the bags from 1 to 10. Take from each bag a number of coins equal to the number of the bag—one coin from bag No. 1, two from bag No. 2, and so forth. Weigh them all together. The result will be light by a number of grams equal to the number of the bag that contains the light coins.

14. A and his wife cross. A returns. B's and C's wives cross. A's returns. B and C cross. B and his wife return. A and B cross. C's wife returns. A's and B's wives cross. C returns. C and his wife cross.

15. The freight trains came six minutes after the passenger trains. Thus the man's odds of arriving after a freight and before a passenger train are 9 to 1, since for fifty-four out of every sixty minutes it is a passenger train that is expected.

16. The numbers 15, 16, and 17 should be placed in groups 3, 3, and 2, respectively. Group 1 consists of numbers composed entirely of curved lines, Group 2 consists of numbers composed entirely of straight lines, and Group 3 consists of numbers composed of a combination of curved and straight lines.

17. The woman has a nine-year-old daughter and two-year-old twins. Since the census taker knew both the product and the sum of their ages, confusion could arise only if two or more sets of ages led to the same product and sum. If we break 36 into three factors we find only two sets of ages (9, 2, 2 and 6, 6, 1) lead to the same sum, 13. The woman's final piece of information tells the census taker that there is only one oldest daughter, not two the same age.

18. House numbers.

19. Nine, two, and two. There are only fourteen combinations of ages that correspond with clues 1 and 2. Since the man solving the puzzle may be presumed to know his own age, the fact that the second clue isn't sufficient to solve the problem shows that his age must be 36—the only product to occur twice. The final clue—that there is only one oldest son, not more—reveals to him that the combination cannot be 6, 6, and 1 but must be 9, 2, and 2.

(This, as you have no doubt realized by this time, is nothing more complicated than a variation of No. 17. I include both because the principle involved seems to me uncommonly interesting.)

CHAPTER III

1.

2. Make two vertical cuts at right angles to each other along the diameters and a horizontal cut through the middle of the cake.

3.

4.

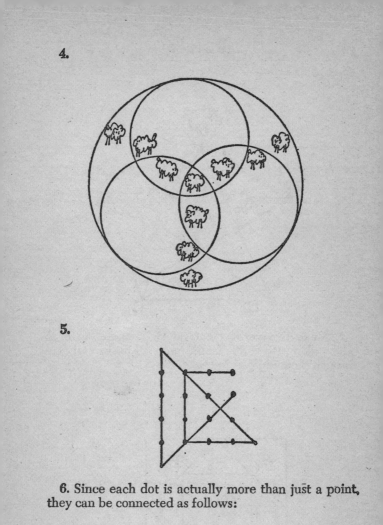

5.

6. Since each dot is actually more than just a point, they can be connected as follows:

7. There are 35 triangles. In alphabetical order, they are: ABC, ABD, ABE, ABF, ABG, ABH, ACD,

ACE, ACI, ADE, ADH, AEF, AEG, AEI, AFG, BCD, BCE, BCG, BCH, BCJ, BDE, BDF, BEJ, BGH, CDE, CDH, CDI, CDJ, CEG, CHJ, DEF, DEI, DEJ, DIJ, and EFI.

 8.

9.

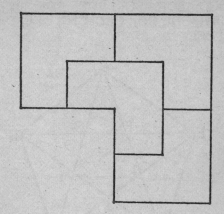

10. The grooves are cut diagonally, as shown:

The block slides apart diagonally.

11.

CAN YOU DRAW A PERFECT SQUARE HAVING ONE DOT ON EACH OF ITS 4 SIDES BUT NO SIDE IS TO TOUCH ANY OF THE WORDS WHICH ARE PRINTED HEREIN? IT IS NOT AS EASY AS IT MAY APPEAR AT FIRST GLANCE.

12.

13. Cut the square and rearrange it this way:

14. Ten inches. Since the path of each pursuer is at all times perpendicular to the path of the pursued, no component of the pursued bug's path moves it closer to or farther from the pursuing bug. The pursuing bug will thus catch up with the pursued bug in exactly the same time it would have taken if the pursued bug had remained stationary. The length of the spiral path is therefore exactly the same as the side of the square, ten inches.

—CHAPTER IV

1. The categories are as follows: AMTUVWY (symmetry about the vertical axis); BCDEK (symmetry about the horizontal axis); FGJLNPQRSZ (no symmetry); and HIOX (symmetry about both axes).

2. *Queueing.*

3. *Witchcraft.*

4. Frederick's message, translated reads: *Dix nez (Dinez) avec moi à cent sous six (Sans Souci),* or "Dine with me at Sans Souci." Voltaire replies: *G grand, à petit (J'ai grand appétit),* or "I have a large appetite."

5. Although the paragraph contains 100 words, the most common letter in the English language—*e*—doesn't appear even once.

6. *Eerie.*

7. *Latchstring.*

8. The letters are *und*. The word is *underground*.

9. "I understand you undertake to undermine by undertaking."

10. *Facetiously* and *abstemiously*.

11. *Indivisibility*.

12. Chances are they haven't. For further confirmation, you might try another short spelling test. It consists of only five words—*kimono, naphtha, iridescent, inoculation,* and *rarefy*—and is in my opinion the toughest brief spelling test ever devised by the mind of man. Even professional editors and writers rarely get more than two or three of the five words right.

13. *Unfortunates—u* as in *view, n* as in *know, f* as in *tough, o* as in *beau, r* as in *myrrh, t* as in *phthisis, u* as in *ewe, n* as in *comptroller, a* as in *neigh, t* as in *light, e* as in *tea,* and *s* as in *psalm*

14. *Stretched.*

15. *Plague.* Remove the first two letters and it becomes *ague.*

16. Water. (H to O, or H_2O)

17.

102004180

(I ought to owe nothing for I ate nothing.)

18. *newsstand, sycamore, subpoena, persimmon, awkward, archeology, perhaps, sovereignty.*

CHAPTER V

1.   15
        36
      +47
      ─────
        98
       +2
      ─────
       100

2. Since one of the terms is $(x-x)$, which equals zero, the answer is zero.

3. The ship is 28 years old. The boiler is 21 years old.

4. The flagpoles are right next to each other.

5. Five, one, and ninety-four, respectively. The answer can be arrived at by starting with these two equations:

$$10C=3S+0.5P=100$$
$$C+S+P=100$$

Because there are two equations but three variables, the problem cannot, of course, be solved without some trial and error. The easiest way is to try different values for C, since the possibilities are more limited than for S and P.

6. $1.19—a half dollar, a quarter, four dimes, and four pennies.

7. The cost of the room was $27 minus $2.00, or $25. The error comes from mistakenly adding $27 and $2.00 and getting the misleading figure of $29. Many readers will recognize this as one of the oldest puzzles around. I include it here because, judging by the numbers of people who write me about it, its vigor remains undiminished in its old age.

8. The problem can be solved in a number of ways. For example, it can be solved somewhat cumbersomely this way: $1+(2\times3)+(4\times5)-6+7+(8\times9)=100$. Or, a bit more neatly: $(1\times2)+34+56+7-8+9=100$. The most elegantly economical solution, however, appears to be this one: $123-45-67+89=100$.

If you still haven't had enough, there are also at least two others.

9.

10. He added his own camel to the original 17, making the division easy:

$\frac{1}{2} \times 18 = 9$

$\frac{1}{3} \times 18 = 6$

$\frac{1}{9} \times 18 = 2$

Since the total is 17, the wise man was then able to take back his own camel and ride on.

11. Square each side:

$$X + \sqrt{X + \sqrt{X + \sqrt{X \dots}}} = 4$$

If, as the problem states—

$$\sqrt{X + \sqrt{X + \sqrt{X \dots}}} = 2$$

—then $X + 2 = 4$.
Therefore $X = 2$.

12. $14—the $6.00 he paid for the watch and the $8 in good money he gave the customer in change. The $20 is of no consequence, since the genuine $20 that the jeweler returned to the storekeeper was offset by the $20 in change that the storekeeper gave the jeweler.

13. Six—five from the original twenty-five cigar butts, and one more once he has smoked the five cigars. L. Y. Wu points out, incidentally, that the hobo can make the six cigars from only twenty-four cigar butts if he first borrows one butt, then returns the last butt to the lender.

14. John has seven apples. Paul has five.

15.

```
    888
     88
      8
      8
     +8
  ─────
  1,000
```

16.

SIX

CHAPTER VI

1. The match.

2. No. It's against the law to bury live people.

3. The third error is that there are only two errors.

4. The one that is not a quarter is a dime. The other one, of course, is a quarter.

5. Fold the edge of the paper as shown:

Then unfold it and complete the figure:

6. No, it isn't legal for a man to marry his widow's sister. Dead people aren't allowed to marry.

7. Of course they have a Fourth of July in England. It's just not a holiday.

8. You don't bury survivors.

9. Moses didn't take any animals onto the ark. Noah did.

10. Put one lump in the first cup, one in the second, and twelve—a very odd number indeed—in the third.

11. All twelve months have twenty-eight days. Some, of course, have more than that, too.

CHAPTER VII

1. This puzzle reveals much about the differences between varying degrees of intelligence. Both the ordinary person and the bright person see one thing clearly right away: that if, for example, a fruit is picked from the box marked "Apples," it can be either an apple or an orange and will therefore tell nothing about whether the box should be marked "Oranges" or "Apples and Oranges." Since the same is true if a fruit is picked from the box marked "Oranges," it is tempting to conclude that the same will also be true of the third box, "Apples and Oranges." But the bright person does not take that supposition for granted. Instead, he goes ahead and tries it. Suppose, he thinks, I pick a fruit from "Apples and Oranges" and it turns out to be an orange—then what do I know about what's in that box? Well, for one thing, since we have been told that all the boxes are wrongly labeled, we know that it is not "Apples and Oranges." Therefore it must be oranges. Then the remaining boxes contain apples and oranges. But which contains which? Simple. Remember once again that the boxes are all mislabeled. Simply switch the two remaining labels and the problem is solved. The bright person has succeeded because he does not assume the problem cannot be solved simply because it cannot be solved in one way or even two ways he has tried. He tries every alternative.

2. They all have three consecutive letters of the alphabet in a row.

3. At first it appears that there is no way, with only one question, to find out (a) if the person asked is the liar or the truthteller and (b) if his fork in the road is the right one or the wrong one. Won't the one question be used up in finding out whether the man is telling the truth or lying, leaving no way to find out the second part of the problem? Apparently so—until it occurs to the puzzler that it may somehow be possible to ask a question whose answer will not depend on which person is asked. Once he is on the trail, the idea of the double falsehood (or double truth, as the case may be) comes easily and he sees that the question to ask is: "If I were to ask you if this is the way I should go, would you say yes?" Interestingly, it doesn't matter which man he asks.

4. Alice, while Matthew had had "had," had had "had had." "Had had" had had a better effect on the teacher.

5. To visualize the problem, imagine that the room can be unfolded, like a shoebox, in various ways and that the routes of the spider to the fly can thus be seen as if they were flat. The apparently straightest route (A) is actually the longest—42 feet. Route B requires that the spider travel slightly over 40 feet. Route C, the shortest, is exactly 40 feet.

6. No. Each domino must cover a black square and a white one. Since any two diagonally opposite squares are the same color, there will always be two uncovered squares left over.

7. Weigh coins 1, 2, 3, and 4 against coins 5, 6, 7, and 8. If they balance, weigh coins 9 and 10 against coins 11 and 8 (we know from the first weighing that 8 is a good coin). If they balance, we know coin 12,

the only unweighed one, is the counterfeit. The third weighing indicates whether it is heavy or light.

If, however, at the second weighing (above), coins 11 and 8 are heavier than coins 9 and 10, either 11 is heavy or 9 is light or 10 is light. Weight 9 with 10. If they balance, 11 is heavy. If they don't balance, either 9 or 10 is light.

Now assume that at first weighing the side with coins 5, 6, 7, and 8 is heavier than the side with coins 1, 2, 3, and 4. This means that either, 1, 2, 3, or 4 is light or 5, 6, 7, or 8 is heavy. Weigh 1, 2, and 5 against 3, 6, and 9. If they balance, it means that either 7 or 8 is heavy or 4 is light. By weighing 7 and 8 we obtain the answer, because if they balance, then 4 has to be light. If 7 and 8 do not balance, then the heavier coin is the counterfeit.

If, when we weigh 1, 2, and 5 against 3, 6, and 9, the right side is heavier, then either 6 is heavy or 1 is light or 2 is light. By weighing 1 against 2 the solution is obtained.

If, however, when we weigh 1, 2, and 5 against 3, 6, and 9, the right side is lighter, then either 3 is light or 5 is heavy. By weighing 3 against a good coin the solution is easily arrived at.

8. The messenger is a truthteller. If the native in the distance lived on the western side of the island, and was therefore a truthteller, he would say so. If, on the other hand, he lived on the eastern side of the island and was therefore a liar, he would say the same thing.

9. Most people erroneously include No. 4. in their answer. But consider: No. 2 does not matter, since the question is concerned only with red cards. If No. 1 has a circle, the answer to the question is no. Similarly, if No. 3 is red the answer is no. If No. 1 is a square, No. 3 is green, and No. 4 is either red or green the answer is yes. Therefore the answer is: No. 1 and No. 3.

10. This is another of those puzzles that at first

glance looks impossible. After all, it appears that the only thing any of the applicants can know is that at least one black mark is visible, and clearly the problem can't be solved on the basis of that piece of information alone. Therefore something else must also be known. But what? Here is where the really intelligent person, rather than feeling defeated, moves into high gear, eventually realizing that he also knows something of the reasoning process that must be going on in the applicants—and that the solution may lie in that fact. Since all three applicants raised their hands, he reasons, there were two possibilities: two black and a white or three black. If, therefore, there were a white mark on any forehead, two men would see one black and one white and would instantly deduce that the third mark must be black. Since this instant solution did not occur, each of the three men saw two black marks. Therefore all were black, including the mark of the successful applicant.

11.

12. The peculiar beauty of this one is that it can be done in an elegantly logical way. It is worth going

through step by step, as an illustration of how an apparently difficult problem yields to a certain sort of mind:

(*a*) The puzzler realizes that, since A multiplied by 4 yields only a one-digit answer, it must be either 1 or 2.

(*b*) Since E×4 must yield an even number, A must be 2.

(*c*) Since the only numbers that, when multiplied by 4, yield a figure ending with 2, are 3 and 8, E must be either 3 or 8.

(*d*) Since A×4 cannot be 13—i.e., cannot be a two-digit number—it must be 8. Therefore E is 8.

(*e*) Since a 3 is carried over to D in the top line, it must also be added to D in the answer. We can see that B×4 must yield a one-digit number. That means that B must be either a 1 or a 2. If it is a 2, then with the 3 added, to it, D would be 11—impossible. So B must be 1.

(*f*) Now consider D. The question here is simple: What number, when multiplied by 4 and enlarged by the carried 3, will yield a number ending in 1? Two numbers fill the bill: 2 and 7. Since we already know that B is 1, the missing number must be 7.

(*g*) The B in the top line must have a carried 3 added to it in order to yield 7 in the answer, so C, when its carried 3 is added to it, must be at least 30. The only numbers that will work, therefore, are 7, 8, or 9. A little experimentation shows that 9 is the missing number.

CHAPTER IX

1. *d*
2. *b*
3. *b*
4. *a*
5. *d*
6. *a*

7. *b*

8. foot

9. *b*

10. *c*

11. *a*

12. *e*

13. *b.* Only Czechoslovakia is landlocked.

14. *a*

15. *c*

16. *c*

17. *d*

18. *a*

19. *a*

20. *b*

21. Barbara has forty, Betty has twenty-four, and Joy has sixteen.

22. *c*

23. *d*

24. *d*

25. *d*

Key to the Mensa test: If you scored more than 24 points, you're definitely Mensa material; from 21 to 23 points, you're very likely Mensa material; from 18 to 20 points, you're a possibility but not a certainty for Mensa; from 15 to 17, you're above average but probably not Mensa material; below 14, see Chapter VIII for puzzle-solving hints.

All Time Bestsellers

- [ ] THE AELIAN FRAGMENT—
  George Bartram   08587-8   1.95
- [ ] THE BERLIN CONNECTION—
  Johannes Mario Simmel   08607-6   1.95
- [ ] THE BEST PEOPLE—Helen Van Slyke   08456-1   1.75
- [ ] A BRIDGE TOO FAR—Cornelius Ryan   08373-5   1.95
- [ ] THE CAESAR CODE—
  Johannes M. Simmel   08413-8   1.95
- [ ] THE CAIN CONSPIRACY—
  Johannes Mario Simmel   08535-5   1.95
- [ ] DO BLACK PATENT LEATHER SHOES
  REALLY REFLECT UP?—John R. Powers   08490-1   1.75
- [ ] THE HAB THEORY—Allen W. Eckerty   08597-5   2.50
- [ ] THE HEART LISTENS—Helen Van Slyke   08520-7   1.95
- [ ] TO KILL A MOCKINGBIRD—Harper Lee   08376-X   1.50
- [ ] THE LAST BATTLE—Cornelius Ryan   08381-6   1.95
- [ ] THE LAST CATHOLIC IN AMERICA—
  J. R. Powers   08528-2   1.50
- [ ] THE LONGEST DAY—Cornelius Ryan   08380-8   1.75
- [ ] THE MIXED BLESSING—Helen Van Slyke   08491-X   1.95
- [ ] THE MONTE CRISTO COVER UP
  Johannes Mario Simmel   08563-0   1.95
- [ ] MORWENNA—Anne Goring   08604-1   1.95
- [ ] THE RICH AND THE RIGHTEOUS
  Helen Van Slyke   08585-1   1.95
- [ ] WEBSTER'S NEW WORLD
  DICTIONARY OF THE AMERICAN
  LANGUAGE   08500-2   1.75
- [ ] WEBSTER'S NEW WORLD THESAURUS   08385-9   1.50
- [ ] THE WORLD BOOK OF HOUSE
  PLANTS—E. McDonald   03152-2   1.50

Buy them at your local bookstores or use this handy coupon for ordering:

Popular Library, P.O. Box 5755, Terre Haute, Indiana 47805   B-5

Please send me the books I have checked above. Orders for less than 5 books must include 60c for the first book and 25c for each additional book to cover mailing and handling. Orders of 5 or more books postage is Free. I enclose $_____ in check or money order.

Name_____

Address_____

City_____ State/Zip_____

Please allow 4 to 5 weeks for delivery. This offer expires 6/78.